WHAT THE PAST
DID FOR US

WHAT THE PAST DID FOR US

DID FOR US

A BRIEF HISTORY OF ANCIENT INVENTIONS

ADAM HART-DAVIS

Published to accompany the television series
What the Past Did for Us, first broadcast on
BBC2 in 2005.

Presenters: Dr Adam Hart-Davis,
Amani Al-Aidroos, Dr Hermione Cockburn,
Jamie Darling and Dr Marty Jopson
Executive producers: John Farren and Martin Mortimore
Series producer: Ian Potts
Producers: Will Aslet, Jane Cameron, Martin Kemp,
Liz Tucker and Patricia Wheatley

ISBN 0 563 52207 0

Published by BBC Books, BBC Worldwide Ltd,
Woodlands, 80 Wood Lane, London W12 0TT

Commissioning editor: Sally Potter
Project editor: Christopher Tinker
Copy-editors: Tessa Clark and Vicki Vrint
Designer: Ann Burnham
Maps and illustrations: Ian Bilbey
Picture researcher: Deirdre O'Day

Set in Minion by BBC Books
Printed and bound in Great Britain by CPI Bath
Colour origination by Butler & Tanner Ltd

For more information on this and other BBC books,
please visit our website at www.bbcshop.com

Publisher's note:
*It is customary to add 'peace be upon him' after every
mention of the prophet Muhammad's name. While this
is not mentioned in Chapter VIII, it is implied.*

CONTENTS

INTRODUCTION

A few years ago I presented a television series about what the Romans did for us, here in Britain – Hadrian's Wall, Portchester Castle, straight roads, and so on. This was followed by what the Victorians, the Tudors, and the Stuarts did for us, and a book to go with each series. But the more I learned about our immediate ancestors, the more I wanted to find out where they got their ideas from. Who were the original thinkers and inventors? This book, and the television series that goes with it, are my attempts to answer that question.

We start in East Anglia with a flint hand-axe that was found on the beach and is about 700,000 years old. It was made not by a human being, *Homo sapiens*, but by an ape-man, *Homo heidelbergensis*, long before anyone in the world settled down or learned to write. The chapter on ancient Britons takes us through the Stone Age, the Bronze Age, and the Iron Age. It explores stone-age monuments, roundhouses, primitive agriculture, and the oldest lavatories in the world.

We then move to Mesopotamia, later the Garden of Eden and now mostly Iraq. The Sumerians and Babylonians, immensely ingenious and practical, developed the plough, and then the seeder plough, two thousand years before the first agricultural machine in the West. They made beer, built the Hanging Gardens of Babylon, and invented the signs of the zodiac that we still use today – Leo, Cancer,

Capricorn, and so on. For me, however, the most extraordinary thing is that they may have made electricity, 1800 years before anyone in Europe.

The Egyptians built pyramids, mummified kings and cats, and crafted superb glass bottles and wooden furniture, not to mention paintings and hieroglyphs on walls and on papyrus. The Indians developed town planning, cast steel, and cotton, and came up with what is perhaps the most important mathematical invention ever – the number zero. The Chinese, isolated from the western world, invented not only paper but also paper money, gunpowder, the wheelbarrow, printing, and silk.

My favourite of all the ancient peoples were the Greeks, who lived in a gaggle of independent city states, scattered around the Mediterranean 'like frogs around a pond', in the words of the great philosopher Plato. The Greeks gave us democracy, theatre, music, and marvellous mathematics, from Pythagoras who invented the musical scale, to Eratosthenes who worked out the size of the Earth in 240 BC.

The Romans pinched Greek technology, improved it, and developed the most impressively organized empire the world has ever seen, complete with sports arenas, aqueducts, bath houses, and communal lavatories.

The Arabs, encouraged by the developing faith of Islam, not only brought masses of eastern wisdom to the West, but also produced many fine inventions of their own, including the camera obscura and the science of optics, irrigation engines, soap, and a galaxy of things beginning with *al-* (from the Arabic) including alchemy, algebra, and alcohol.

Finally, the Mayas, the Aztecs and the Incas developed entirely separate ways of life in Central and South America. They flourished until they were wiped out by Spanish biological warfare in the sixteenth century. We have the Mesoamericans to thank for chocolate, rubber, tobacco, and quinine.

As usual, I have spent this year on a steep learning curve, fascinated to find out about the distant past. I hope that you too are interested in what those ancients did for us.

Adam Hart-Davis
July 2004

I

THE BRITONS

The Romans arrived in Britain, determined to stay, in AD 43. The Britons saw the new arrivals as invaders and fought hard against their conquest. The Romans saw the Britons as uncouth, trouser-wearing savages isolated on a damp and misty island far from the centre of the cultured world. They imagined that they were bringing civilization, advanced technologies and an appreciation of the arts to a backward land. Well, in one respect they were right – Britain was undeniably much damper than Rome and the awful weather forced the sun-loving Roman soldiers to adopt socks for the first time ever. But in all other respects they were very wrong. Britain had already passed through three technological ages: the Stone Age, the Bronze Age and the Iron Age. It was a well-organized and well-fed land with complex political hierarchies, an established priesthood and strong trading links with Europe. And all this with a population that couldn't read or write!

Britain's first tool-kit

By the time of the Roman invasion Britain was an island. This had not always been the case. Throughout the last ice age it had been sporadically attached to Europe. The term 'ice age' is a misleading one. True, there were times of bitter cold when the ice sheets completely covered northern Britain. But there were also periods when the climate was warmer than today, dense woodlands grew and hunter-gatherers wandered across grassy plains crossing non-existent national boundaries. These hunter-gatherers belonged to the Palaeolithic, or Old Stone Age, culture – a very long cultural stage that covers well over 95 per cent of human history.

Britain's oldest known inhabitant is a half-million-year-old man found at Boxgrove, West Sussex. His meagre remains – a shin bone and two teeth (from different individuals) – prove that he lived long before Neanderthal man (*Homo sapiens neanderthalensis*) and modern man (*H. sapiens sapiens*). He has been given the name *H. heidelbergensis* after an ancient jaw discovered near Heidelberg, Germany. Today the Boxgrove site is a gravel pit turned conservation site, but half a million years ago it was a fertile plain at the base of a cliff. Here a hunter-gatherer band lived. Their kill, which included giant deer, rhinoceros and horse, was butchered using stone tools that the hunters made as they squatted around the carcass. These tools, known as handaxes or bifaces, were well made and varied in design, suggesting good manual dexterity and a well-developed brain.

An even earlier handaxe has been recovered from the Norfolk coast between Yarmouth and Cromer. When Mike Chambers left home to take his dog for a walk along the beach he did not imagine that he was just about to discover the oldest known tool in the British Isles. But there it was, sticking out of a muddy area in the cliff, a fist-sized lump of shaped stone with a still-sharp point (see plates, page 2). Archaeologists later discovered a second artefact, an animal bone with traces of cut-marks, at the same place in the cliff. The position of the two finds, low down the cliff face, suggests they may date to between 600,000 and 700,000 years ago. Experts believe that they, too, were made by *Homo heidelbergensis*.

Handaxes were not simply axes. They were the ancient equivalent of the Swiss army knife – multipurpose tools with a razor-sharp continuous edge that could be used for killing, skinning and cleaning animals, cutting and whittling wood plus, probably, scores of other uses that we cannot begin to imagine. The best British examples are made from flint, a hard but brittle glass-like stone that breaks in a highly predictable way. Given the poor survival rates of organic material such as wood and bone, the understanding of stone tools is essential to comprehending this early stage in Britain's development. So, how were they made?

The art of making a flint tool is called knapping. Manufacture started with the choice of a suitably sized nodule of flint. The knapper then roughed out a basic handaxe, using a pebble hammer to knock short, thick flakes off the flint. Next he used a softer hammer made from an animal bone or antler to detach longer, more delicate flakes until the flint was pared down to the required shape. When satisfied the knapper would move on, taking the handaxe and leaving behind a heap of unwanted flakes. Sounds easy, doesn't it? But knapping takes years of practice, and the sharp flint can cause some nasty cuts.

Hundreds of thousands of years later, Neanderthalers had arrived in Britain and they, too, were making stone tools. They rejected the large-scale handaxe, preferring to use a more compact, rounded version plus a variety of lighter tools made from the flakes struck off

Ancient Britons fashioned simple hand tools from stone, animal bones and antlers.

the flint cores. At Lynford Quarry, again in Norfolk, archaeologists have discovered the remains of a dozen mammoths, a bear, a woolly rhino, deer, and over 30 typical Neanderthal handaxes. It isn't known whether the Neanderthalers actually hunted and killed the mammoths, which would have been frighteningly large and fierce, or whether they simply acted as scavengers. It is known that they stripped meat off the deer bones, because the bones carry telltale cut-marks. And we can guess that they put their animal products to good use – not just as food, but also as sources of leather, sinew, antler and fur.

The trend towards smaller, lighter tool-kits continued with the arrival of modern man and the ending of the ice age. The Mesolithic people (Middle Stone Age, 8000–4000 BC) made tiny stone tools called microliths. They no longer hunted much big game because there wasn't much big game left for them to hunt. They lived in forests, by rivers or the sea, where they shot small animals with flint-tipped arrows – the bow and arrow was a recent addition to their weaponry – and fished with bone fish hooks and harpoons. Plants and shellfish played an important role in their diet, oysters being a special favourite – modern archaeologists have great fun excavating their vast shell middens or rubbish heaps. The Mesolithic people did make axes and adzes, but these were specialist woodworking tools designed to be fitted with a wooden or antler handle.

The arrival of farming marks the start of the British Neolithic (New Stone Age), in approximately 4000 BC. By now Britain was an island accessible only by boat. The Neolithic flint tool-kit included axes, adzes, arrowheads and a range of small-scale scrapers, borers and points. Good-quality flint was in great demand, and Grimes Graves, Norfolk, became the centre of British flint production. Here the miners sank mineshafts, then dug galleries to reach the chalk that carried the seams of flint. Flint nodules were prized out of the chalk with mattocks made from antlers, and hauled to the surface in baskets.

Flint was not the only stone in demand at this time. In the north and west of the country there were axe factories where local fine-grained stones were used in the manufacture of ground and polished axes, mace heads and adzes.

The first housing estate

By the end of the Neolithic period Britain was a sophisticated land of farmsteads, land enclosures and ritual monuments criss-crossed by trade networks that today are almost invisible. Where did these traders live? Mainland Britain has yielded various sequences of postholes that represent the remains of long-vanished rectangular wooden farmhouses. But the best evidence for Neolithic housing comes from the Scottish islands.

In 1850 a violent storm hit the Orkneys, a group of islands off the north-east tip of Scotland. On the western edge of the main island (Mainland) turf was ripped off the sand dunes, exposing a Late Neolithic housing estate. Skara Brae is a bleak and windswept site, and the eight or more Neolithic houses nestled together in semi-subterranean hollows that offered protection from the harsh elements. They were linked by roofed, dry-stone-wall passages, so there was no need to get wet when visiting the neighbours. A shortage of timber meant the Neolithic builders were forced to use slabs of local stone, not just for the floors and walls but for their furniture too. Turf, or maybe whale ribs covered with animal hides, was used for roofing.

If you walk into the Skara Brae houses today you will see the original hearths, cupboards, shelving and even beds, all made of stone. The design of all the interiors is the same, with a central hearth, beds on either side of the entrance and a dresser facing the door (see plates, page 1). Stone storage boxes held the grasses and furs that made the hard, cold beds comfortable, while stone tanks lined with clay stored limpets for use as fishing bait. For me, one of the most remarkable features of these houses is that they each have an en-suite lavatory, with underground drains leading down towards the sea. They are arguably the oldest known lavatories in the world.

Here, for six hundred years, the Neolithic people lived in harmony – fishing, hunting, keeping cattle and sheep, and, to a limited extent, cultivating grain. They made bone tools, stone sculptures, shell beads and pots. But Skara Brae was eventually abandoned. It was soon covered in the windblown sand that would preserve it for over four thousand years.

The first boats

Britain may have been an island, but it was by no means isolated. A complex network of trade routes tied it to the continent in the Neolithic period (4000–2500 BC) and Bronze Age (2500–800 BC), and archaeologists have unearthed numerous finds of pottery and metal to confirm that Britain was becoming increasingly familiar with foreign goods. A Bronze Age shipwreck discovered to the east of Dover harbour has given us the Langdon Bay hoard, a cargo of over 95 bronze objects of French origin. These were not high-quality retail goods, but scrap metal that was being sent to Britain for recycling. A second wreck, off the coast at Salcombe, Devon, gave two palstaves (bronze chisels), a sword blade and four other blades, again of continental origin. Meanwhile, finds of Cornish pottery in France are a reminder that goods were being traded in two directions.

Of course, exchange was not limited to physical goods. Ideas, too, passed backwards and forwards over the water, so British burial urns and stone circles have their closest parallels in Belgium and France. Archaeologists have been able to identify three main trade routes: the Atlantic seaboard route (linking west Scotland, Wales, Ireland, France and Spain); the North Sea zone (connecting East Anglia to Holland and Belgium); and the Dover–Calais channel crossing between south-east England and France. Today these can be rough crossings, particularly in winter. In Bronze Age times sailors would have enjoyed better weather, with fewer strong winds leading to fewer storms at sea.

Sea routes needed seaworthy ships. This was no problem – Bronze Age people were accomplished carpenters, and a great deal of Britain's internal trade was already being conducted by water. As yet no complete British Bronze Age seagoing ship has been discovered, but there are the remains of four plank-built boats. Three substantial fragments were found in what may well be Britain's earliest boatyard, on the muddy shore of the Humber estuary at North Ferriby, Humberside. These are the earliest surviving European vessels of their kind; it seems likely that they were used as ferries for taking people, goods and animals across the wide Humber River. A major part of another boat has recently been recovered from Dover. Each of these boats was sewn – the planks were stitched together with tough woody fibres (metal nails had yet to be invented!) – and each was designed to be paddled. The Dover boat has been radiocarbon-dated to 1550 BC, and is therefore a thousand years younger than the more sophisticated boat from the reign of the pharaoh Khufu in Egypt (see page 51).

The earliest of these ancient vessels is the first Ferriby boat, discovered by Ted Wright in 1937. I have walked along the shore with Ted, and he told me just how he had made the discovery.

The first Ferriby boat, which was made around 1900 BC, was discovered in the Humber estuary in 1937.

He and his brother were wandering along the muddy bank of the Humber looking for artefacts – the scouring action of the river continually shifts the contours of the mud and so from time to time reveals buried objects. Ted suddenly saw a stitched plank poking through the mud, and called to his brother, 'Hey, I think I've found a Viking ship!' His brother came running over and said, 'By Jove, I think you have!' They were even more astonished to hear that the boat long predated the Vikings.

Ted obviously had a knack for boat-finding. Three years later, on leave from the army, he discovered a second boat close by. The third would be found, in the same mud, in 1963. The first boat is represented by most of its flat bottom plus a length of the strake on one side; the complete vessel would have been over 15 metres long and over 2 metres wide. It is made from oak planks up to 10 cm (4 in) thick sewn together edge-to-edge with yew branches, then caulked with moss. Oak batons were slid under the yew to make sure the boat remained watertight. The planks show traces left by ancient woodworking tools: two different sizes of adze, a heavy knife and an auger to bore the stitch-holes.

Plank-built boats required a considerable investment of time and specialized labour, and a large amount of wood. They were way beyond the reach of the ordinary man or woman in the field. Britain's earliest, and most frequently used, vessels were simple rafts and more advanced coracles – purely British developments that were ideal for rivers, lakes and short trips to islands. Unfortunately none of these vessels has survived, although several log-boat canoes have.

Settlement and farming

Boats linked neighbouring communities, making long-distance trade possible. For Britain had become a land of settled farmers, and with this development came a huge change in lifestyle. Nomadic hunting groups have to transport everything they own. Settled farmers are free to accumulate belongings, and so settlement goes hand in hand with increasing material wealth and an increasing use of pottery.

The move towards farming was gradual. Early Neolithic people had access to exciting new resources, including wheat and barley, which are not native to Britain. They also had domesticated cattle, pigs and sheep/goats – archaeologists can't always tell the difference and so tend to lump these two together as one beast, a shoat perhaps, or a geep! But they still hunted, gathered wild crops and fished. Many people adopted a semi-nomadic way of life, living in movable tents or shelters rather than permanent stone and wooden houses. It was in the Bronze Age that settlement and social stratification – the division between the rich and influential and the poor and socially unimportant – became obvious.

Farming certainly had a dramatic effect on the environment. As the Neolithic period slid seamlessly into the Bronze Age, acres of forests were cleared to make way for cereal crops and grazing, and the new idea of landownership was emphasized by the building of impressive monuments. Large-scale Neolithic enclosures, ringed by ditches and embankments, must have been visible for miles around. Now the dead also started to claim their fair share of the land, for Britain's first formal cemeteries date from this time.

The best evidence for plant cultivation comes from seeds and grains accidentally pressed into prehistoric pottery. These show that different crops were grown in different areas, with wheat being particularly well suited to conditions in the south, and barley dominant in the north. The earliest farmers used simple scratch ploughs, or ards, to break up their land. None of these has survived but, remarkably, some of their furrows have. Under the South Street long barrow, near Avebury, Wiltshire, are the criss-cross marks left by a Neolithic plough – archaeologists know the marks are Neolithic, because they can date the barrow that covers and protects them. At Gwithian in Cornwall, and Rosinish on the island of Benbecula, off the west coast of Scotland, early Bronze Age farmers also cross-ploughed their fields, presumably using a stone-tipped wooden ard pulled by one or two oxen. The plough marks have lasted for over four thousand years because they were made in areas now considered too bleak or too remote to be farmed.

Once the plough had broken up the land any further necessary tilling was done by hand using a wooden hoe or spade. At harvest time the crops were gathered with a reaping knife or sickle. Flint sickles carry a characteristic 'sickle gloss', a shiny area along their cutting edge that proves they were used to harvest grasses or cereals. The ears of corn were threshed and winnowed, and the grain was stored for up to two years in mud- or clay-lined airtight pits. The first archaeologists to discover prehistoric storage pits misinterpreted them as curious, windowless underground housing.

To make bread, grain was taken from the pit, cleaned and then ground into flour on a stone quern or grinding stone. The earliest of these were simple saddle querns – a saddle- or saucer-shaped lower stone over which the grain was spread, and a smaller, rounded upper stone, or rider, that was rubbed backwards and forwards over the grain to grind it. Saddle querns are effective but labour-intensive, and can cause a nasty backache in the user! The development of the rotary quern during the Iron Age (800 BC–AD 43) probably allowed a tenfold increase in production rates. The rotary quern had a heavy lower stone with a socket for a spindle, and a doughnut-shaped upper one which fitted over the spindle and was turned using a socketed handle. Until recently, in Portugal a rotary quern was valued as a traditional wedding gift – it would last a lifetime, and would be handed down from generation to generation.

Roundhouses and monuments

Bronze Age and Iron Age farmers lived in large circular huts or roundhouses built with strong wooden posts to hold up the heavy thatched roofs. This is known because as the wooden posts rotted away they left very obvious, house-sized circles of holes. So reconstructing the basic shape of the roundhouse is easy. Reconstructing the long-vanished walls and roofs involves a great deal of guesswork, however. Wattle and daub, dry-stone walling, wooden posts and wooden planks could all be used to fill in the walls between the posts. Archaeologists generally assume that the roofs were conical, but cannot be absolutely certain. A conical roof would certainly give a roundhouse great strength and stability – it would push downwards on to the walls, and the ground would act as a counter-thrust to the weight of the building and a lateral anchor for any freestanding posts. The trick was to get the right angle for the roof.

This is one area where experimental archaeology can be useful. Butser Ancient Farm, Hampshire, is an open-air centre set up to investigate all aspects of Iron Age farming. Here several roundhouses of various sizes have been re-created. This has allowed archaeologists to test their theories in a practical way – and has often shown how things could not possibly have been done. The Great Roundhouse is based on an authentic plan excavated at Longbridge Deverill, Wiltshire; it is an impressive 15 metres in diameter, and built with a double ring of structural posts. The inner ring of uprights, strengthened by a horizontal ring of timber, holds up the conical thatched roof, which is supported on six main rafters. The outer ring is part of the wattle-and-daub exterior. The inside of the house has been difficult to reconstruct, although the position of the hearth is known. The gap between the two rings of posts may well have been subdivided to make storerooms or bedrooms, and it is even possible that an internal platform or gallery may have offered two-storey living.

Not all roundhouses had a double ring of posts. Some had a single one, with the weight of the roof supported by the wall head; and sometimes, but not always, these houses have a central post. And by no means all roundhouses were as large as the Great Roundhouse at Butser. Some were single-room houses for poorer families, some were individual 'rooms' in a larger complex, some were storage facilities and some may even have been religious shrines.

Although early Britons were very practical – they grew crops, built houses and boats, made pots and stone tools, and traded a wide range of goods with their neighbours – there was a well-developed spiritual side to their nature, shown by the attention they lavished on the burial of their dead – we can understand this, because we too have to cope with the death and burial of loved ones. Barrows (large and long) may have had both a practical (corpse disposal) and a ritual purpose. The standing stones and ceremonial circles (henges) raised at about the same time as the barrows have a less obvious religious function and remain something of a mystery.

Everyone has heard of Stonehenge, the Neolithic and Early Bronze Age stone circle in Wiltshire. Not everyone realizes that it is by no means Britain's only henge monument. In fact, over 900 stone circles have been identified there and in Ireland, widely distributed from Callanish on Lewis in the Outer Hebrides, to Mount Pleasant in Dorset. They range in date from perhaps 3000 BC to 1600 BC – an amazing time span of 1400 years. In addition there are numerous stone-less earth-bank circles, and the relatively recent science of aerial photography has revealed circular arrangements of now-empty postholes – the remains of wooden henges.

So how was Stonehenge constructed? It is a complex and composite monument built in several stages:

Phase 1 *A bank with an external ditch surrounding a ring of 56 timber posts was built. The remains of the postholes, known today as Aubrey holes, were later used for cremation burials. One outlying stone, the 'heel stone' marked the entrance to the circle.*

Phase 2 *A series of wooden posts was raised in the centre of the monument. Digging the pits for the later stones disturbed so much ground that it is hard to work out what they represented.*

Phase 3 *Later, the site was remodelled – 82 bluestones were transported by boat from the Preseli hills in Wales, a 200-km (125-mile) journey, and erected in a double horseshoe or a double circle. An avenue led to the circle. This phase may never have been finished.*

Phase 4 *The bluestones were taken down. A circle of 30 sarsen (sandstone) blocks from the nearby Marlborough Downs was raised and topped by a continuous ring of lintels held in place with mortise and tenon joints. Inside the stone circle was a U-shaped arrangement of five pairs of massive stones, each with a lintel (the 'trilithons'). Further phases of remodelling saw the bluestones re-erected inside the sarsen circle.*

Of course, detailing the phases gets us no nearer to understanding how such heavy stones were raised. Experimental archaeologists have struggled to re-create Stonehenge with frames, pulleys and a great deal of manpower.

The monument is famously aligned to the summer solstice (the longest day of the year, when the sun is at its furthest distance from the equator) so that the midsummer sunrise shines down the axis of the site. It is also aligned to the midwinter sunset – the end of the shortest day of the year. Archaeologists generally accept that it could have functioned as an observatory. Some experts have taken this to mean that Stonehenge was a temple dedicated to the god of the sun or the sky. Others have interpreted the site as a form of calendar that could have been used to confirm the timing of religious rituals related to fertility and the agricultural year.

The behaviour of the life-giving sun would always be of interest to a farming community dependent on good weather for decent crops, and other prehistoric sites have obvious astronomical alignments. At New Grange in the Boyne valley, Ireland, a Neolithic passage tomb was built so that the rising sun at the winter solstice shines down the passage into the burial chamber.

Meanwhile at Callanish, remote on the western edge of the Outer Hebrides, there are more than 20 sets of stones in a couple of square miles. The main circle has 13 stones – slender, white and pointed, like teeth reaching for the sky. There is a central, taller stone and four incomplete avenues. This complex arrangement seems to have been built to celebrate the 'major standstill' of the moon. Once every 18.6 years the full moon (as seen from the main circle) rises over the Sleeping Beauty mountain; it 'rolls' almost along the horizon, and sets between the stones, as seen from the end of the major avenue.

To plan a monument aligned with the midsummer sunrise you would have to watch the sun rising day after day, and align its position with poles in the ground. This might take 10 years, but you could be certain of your alignments. At Callanish, however, you would have to rely on stories from your parents and grandparents even to know about the moon's curious manoeuvre; and to check the exact alignments would take at least one lifetime. What is more, although Stonehenge may have been built at least partly for agricultural reasons, this cannot be the case with Callanish, since the major standstill has no connection with any particular season. The next one will happen in the early months of 2006.

Gold and power dressing

Bush Barrow is one of a cluster of early Bronze Age barrows lying about half a mile to the south of Stonehenge. When opened in 1808, it yielded a male skeleton, a bronze axe, two bronze daggers, a copper dagger, a stone mace head (the remains of a sceptre?), a gold belt-fastener (the belt had perished), a diamond-shaped gold breastplate and a small gold lozenge. The dead man had been a person of great importance, maybe a priest or a tribal chief, and he had been buried with grave goods appropriate to his status.

The Bronze Age may have been named after an unexciting utilitarian metal (bronze: an alloy of copper and tin). But gold, less practical but infinitely more beautiful, was the one in demand. This was an age of ostentatious personal adornment and power dressing – those who could afford it wore it and flaunted it. Alongside necklaces of jet and amber beads there are basket-shaped gold earrings, gold buttons and over 80 gold *lunulae* (singular *lunula*). These crescent-shaped collars made from decorated sheet gold have been found in Ireland, Scotland and south-west England. A unique gold cape was recovered from a burial in Mold, Clwyd, which also yielded a necklace of amber beads. The love of gold continued into the Iron Age, when gold *lunulae* were replaced by torcs – metal neck rings – frequently with a twisted design and often associated with Celtic warriors (see plates, page 1).

Perhaps this increasing emphasis on personal adornment is a sign of developing social stratification – the emergence of an upper class whose official jewellery marked them out as special people. Or it may simply be that certain individuals, the *nouveaux riches* who had accumulated wealth through trade, were becoming less conformist in their dress. It may even be that the gold ornaments were ceremonial items reserved for rituals and burials. Certainly, gold was not used only for jewellery. In 1837 the Rillaton gold cup – a small ribbed cup made from sheet gold – was found beneath a large round barrow on Bodmin Moor, Cornwall. It was claimed by the royal family, and for several years it was used to hold George V's collar studs. It is now in the British Museum, along with its near twin, the Ringlemere gold cup, which was discovered near Sandwich in Kent in 2001. The two cups are so alike they may have been made by the same craftsman, even though they were found nearly 650 km (400 miles) apart.

Gold, unlike all the other metals exploited in prehistory, is so malleable that it can be worked cold. Beating a nodule of the metal will flatten it to a thin sheet, which can be shaped by hammering or twisting and then decorated with piercings, punchings or engravings. Ireland, with impressive supplies of gold in the Wicklow hills, was the centre of Bronze Age gold production; today the National Museum of Ireland has the largest collection of gold work from this period in the British Isles. However, not all of it was made in Ireland, and not all the gold used was Irish.

Spectrographic analysis allows scientists to examine the composition of gold, which includes traces of other metals including copper. If the make-up of a prehistoric metal can be profiled, it can be matched to its source. It is also possible to source finished gold objects by recognizing the styles and techniques of the ancient craftsmen. The classic *lunulae* made by the sophisticated Irish craftsmen are obviously different from those made by the provincial workmen in Scotland, Wales, Cornwall and Brittany; so if a classic *lunula* is found outside Ireland it is likely to be an export.

The arms race

Gold was a soft metal of little practical use. The first workaday metal to be exploited in Britain, using techniques copied from Europe, was copper. Luckily, Britain and Ireland had many rich deposits of copper ores – four thousand years ago the world's largest copper mine was on the Welsh coast at Great Orme, Llandudno. Here the workers dug with bone, antler and possibly bronze tools, sinking shafts and galleries to a depth of at least 70 metres. Miles of passages cover an area of over 24,000 sq metres – just imagine how much ore must have been extracted!

Copper ore was smelted in a small, open-bowl furnace fuelled by charcoal and kept going with bellows made from skin. The molten metal collected in the bottom of the furnace in a 'cake' of blister copper that was full of air holes caused by the gases formed during smelting. The cake was reheated in a crucible, stirred with a green wooden bough to remove impurities, and then poured into a simple one-piece stone or fired-clay mould to make a flat axe or a dagger. Later the development of the three-piece mould made hollow castings possible; craftsmen were now able to make a socketed metal tool that could be attached to a wooden handle.

From around 2500 BC ancient Britons made durable weapons, including spear heads, shields and helmets, out of bronze.

Metalworkers soon found they could make a far stronger metal by adding a little tin – a good mixture as bronze was one part tin to eight parts copper. Luckily, western Britain was rich not only in copper; there were also good supplies of tin. Bronze Age technology arrived in the country in 2500 BC and with it came the race to find ever more efficient weapons. Daggers lengthened into rapiers; rapiers were replaced by slashing swords. Bronze-headed spears were used for throwing as javelins or for hand-to-hand combat. Alongside these there were round, leather shields with bronze studs, and bronze helmets to protect the warriors. Such weapons and defensive armour have been found throughout Britain, and some are beautiful.

The most commonly used weapon was the rapier. So how was it made? The simplest method was lost-wax casting:

1. *The rapier was modelled in beeswax.*
2. *The beeswax model was covered in clay, leaving an access hole.*
3. *The mould was heated until the wax melted and could be poured out through the hole.*
4. *The bronze was heated and poured into the mould through the access hole.*
5. *The mould was cooled and broken open to reveal the bronze rapier.*
6. *The rapier was trimmed, ground, and polished.*

Bronze had many more practical uses than copper, but supplies of copper and tin were limited and this made it more expensive than copper, and in 800 BC the arrival of iron opened up new possibilities. The tools made from this metal were not much stronger than their bronze predecessors, but iron ore was widely available and therefore relatively cheap to use – there was no longer any need for deep mines. This is not cast iron as we know it from the Industrial Revolution. Prehistoric metallurgists used bowl furnaces, and could not raise temperatures high enough to melt the iron (about 1500°C) and produce cast goods, as they had with copper. But they could reach temperatures of 1100–1150°C, high enough to extract the iron from its ore. The resultant spongy mass, the 'bloom', was forged by repeated heating and hammering. The blacksmith needed strength and skill to hit the metal in the right place while it was red-hot, and to make what later came to be called wrought iron.

This new metal made good strong sickles and ploughshares and swords. This was an age of strong territorial identity; communities developed and settled – often in fortified settlements or hill forts – and needed to protect themselves from marauders.

Barter and coinage

By the end of the first century BC Britain was part of a wide European economic trading network. The Greek geographer Strabo lists its principal exports: gold, grain, cattle, silver, iron, hides, slaves and dogs. In exchange, it seems that Britain was importing large quantities of wine, unworked glass and figs or fig seeds. This is interesting to prehistorians who, if this list didn't exist, would have great trouble detecting many of these dealings. Wine trading is often made obvious by the presence of wine jars, and if there really was a slave trade this may explain finds of iron chains, but without Strabo how would we ever know that Britain exported dogs or had an insatiable demand for figs?

How did Iron Age people pay for their goods? Well, the vast majority of their transactions were done by barter – a straightforward swapping system useful for goods of equal value. But it could be awkward. It depended on each of two people having something the other wanted. The man who wanted to swap five baskets of grain for three baskets of fish might lug his heavy produce all the way to the harbour only to find that the fisherman had enough grain, and really needed furs. Under these circumstances it is unlikely that the farmer would receive the full asking price for his grain – he might well have to go home with just one basket of fish.

A better method was to use some kind of token – maybe a small metal ingot, or possibly a flat metal axe – which everyone would recognize and accept. The farmer could take two tokens to the harbour and acquire his fish; the fisherman would have the tokens to spend on furs at his leisure. This system was adopted all over Europe, and thousands of what may be tokens have been found on a trade route between England, France and Spain.

Britain was the last important region of western Europe to adopt coinage, but by the time Julius Caesar wrote about his wartime experiences there (55–54 BC) he was able to tell his readers that the Britons 'use either bronze or gold coinage, or else iron bars of definite weight instead of coins'. Britain had received her first regular imports of gold Gallo-Belgic coins in 150 BC. Local imitations started 50 years later when blanks were cast in clay moulds, then individually struck between dies. The earliest coins were made of bronze; gold coins started in about 80 BC. Experts disagree over the interpretation of this development. Is it is a clear case of Romanization, with the Britons blindly copying everything the Romans did? Or is it a sign that Iron Age Britain was now a powerful economic unit

Britons were using bronze or gold coins by the first century BC.

starting to find its own identity? After all, a coin complete with the head and name of a tribal chief could be a useful propaganda tool.

Soon each of the powerful British tribes had its own inscribed coins whose texts were written in the Latin alphabet, just as they were on contemporary Roman ones. This first recorded use of writing signals Britain's transition from prehistory to history. The names of long-dead chiefs can be read on their coins and we can recognize Tasciovanus, chief of the Catavellauni and Trinovantes tribes, and his son Cunobelinus, father to Caratacus and Togidubnus. Cunobelinus was a highly influential chief who is described as 'REX' or king on his coins, which also show images of horse-drawn chariots.

Chariots

Once British men started riding horses they began wearing the trousers that so shocked the toga- and tunic-wearing Romans. Increasing finds of harness fittings – bits and rein rings made from iron and bronze – show just how important horses had become by the late Iron Age. The first indication of horse-drawn transport came from cemeteries in East Yorkshire. Here there developed a tradition of burying vehicles with their owners. This was common in northern France and western Germany, but rare in Britain, where only 19 such burials are known, and all but one of these are in Yorkshire.

Experts usually describe these as 'carts' to distinguish them from Roman-style racing chariots (think *Ben Hur*), but this conjures up images of large, lumbering everyday vehicles that were perhaps used on a farm. The excavated examples and pictures on coins confirm that these were lighter vehicles with two spoked wheels, a fixed axle and a rectangular boxed platform for the driver and passengers, drawn by two ponies yoked on either side of a pole. Their inclusion in elite graves shows that they were not for everyday use. To all intents and purposes, whether or not they were ever intended to be used on the battlefield, they are chariots.

Three chariot burials – the bodies were those of two men and a woman – were excavated in a quarry at Wetwang Slack. All the burials were the same: first the two wheels were placed in the grave, then the corpse laid on these, then personal grave goods – a sword, shield and spear for each of the men, and, for the woman, a mirror, a pin, a workbox and a joint of pork, perhaps food for her journey to the afterlife. Finally, the rest of the vehicle was placed on top of the body.

In 2001 another was discovered within Wetwang itself. This was the grave of another woman and, once more, it included a dismantled vehicle, an iron mirror and a joint of pork. Unfortunately, all the wood had rotted and was detectable only through slight changes in the soil. The chariot was reconstructed by the BBC, who looked at other evidence from Britain and the European mainland to fill in the gaps left by the vanished wood. As early Britons were famed for their love of colour, the finished vehicle was painted with natural pigments. It was then tested with horses trained to the Iron Age yoke system. The test was highly successful, proving that the chariot functioned well with the driver either sitting or standing, even when the horses galloped.

Three hundred years after the Wetwang woman died, Julius Caesar launched a punitive raid against the Kentish tribes who were supporting the Gauls in their fight against Roman imperialism. He was highly impressed by British fighting tactics and the effective use they made of their charioteers: 'They start by driving all over the field and throwing their javelins. Then they jump down from their chariots and fight on foot.' Sometimes, he tells us, thousands of chariots rode together; they must have made a fearful noise, striking fear into the hearts of the Roman foot soldiers. As the warriors fought, their chariots were parked nearby so that they could beat a quick retreat if necessary. Even allowing for Caesar's need to exaggerate – after all, he had to let the folks back home know exactly why he had failed to subdue the barbarians – this suggests impressive chariot expertise. Caesar was perhaps lucky that he lived a century before Britain's most famous charioteer: Boudicca.

II

THE MESOPOTAMIANS

Mesopotamia is from the Greek for 'between the rivers', and refers to the fertile lowlands between the Tigris and Euphrates, stretching from northern Syria south-east to the Persian Gulf. More than any other, this region was the cradle of civilization; the Sumerian people, who inhabited Sumer, the southern half of the country, were prodigious innovators who laid the foundations of an advanced, technological society. More than five thousand years ago, they developed villages into complex city states that were home to thousands of citizens. These were typically centred around a stepped pyramid called a ziggurat, where the city's personal god was believed to live.

Each city was surrounded by massive brick-built walls. There was no stone to speak of in Mesopotamia, so the Sumerians made their own in the form of characteristic concave-faced, fired bricks. As well as many good things, such as writing, the plough, irrigation, the wheel and beer, the Sumerians also gave us truly organized warfare, with a professional army and siege weapons.

They seem to have been immigrants from the East. No one knows their original home, and their language is likewise a mystery. It is not related to any of the Semitic ones in the area, nor to the Indo-European group to which most European languages belong. Sumerian, like the people who spoke it, appears to be unique.

To the north of Sumer lay Akkad, home of the Akkadians. These people eventually came to rule over the whole of Mesopotamia. They

maintained much of Sumerian civilization and built on its founda-
tions, as did other rulers in following centuries. The Babylonian,
Assyrian and Persian empires, which conquered much of the Middle
East, all owe much to the early innovations of the Sumerians.

Managing water

The fabled city of Babylon impressed all who saw it; Herodotus,
the father of history, was moved to write in 450 BC that 'Babylon
surpasses in splendour any city in the known world'. He described
the city's outer walls as being 90 km (60 miles) in circumference,
100 metres high, and 25 metres thick, wide enough to allow a four-
horse chariot to turn. Behind the inner walls lay bastions and
dwellings, and temples holding massive statues of solid gold. The
ziggurat to the god Marduk, thought by some to be the origin of the
legend of the Tower of Babel, dominated the city, pointing like a
huge finger towards heaven.

But for all its grandeur, one person had been distinctly under-
whelmed by the city. In 650 BC Babylon's king was Nebuchadnezzar,
and he had recently married Amyitis, a princess of the northern
mountainous kingdom of Media. Impressive as it was, Babylon
lay on the flat alluvial plain of the Euphrates, and the view from
the palace window was boring. Queen Amyitis was homesick – she

longed for the hills of her native land, and pined for the wooded slopes of Media.

And so, for love of his new wife, Nebuchadnezzar ordered an artificial mountain to be built, complete with trees and flowing streams – a structure that became one of the Seven Wonders of the Ancient World: the Hanging Gardens of Babylon. 'Hanging' probably gives a false impression of the edifice. Nothing was suspended by cables or ropes; the word derives from the Greek word *kremastos* which could mean not simply 'hanging', but 'overhanging'. 'The Balconied (or Terraced) Gardens of Babylon' would be a more accurate translation, though neither has the poetic ring of the traditional title.

Diodorus Siculus, writing in the first century BC, records that this artificial mountain was about 130 metres square and rose to a height of 25 metres. Other accounts claim that it was as high as the city walls, which Herodotus claimed to be 1000 metres high. Whatever the actual size, the hanging gardens were undoubtedly an arresting sight – a verdant, forested mountain rising majestically from the flat, dusty and otherwise monotonous plains of Mesopotamia. Apart from pleasing his wife, the gardens performed an important propaganda function. They advertised Babylon's might in no uncertain

The shaduf is a simple water-lifting machine. A bucket hung from the end of a pivoted beam, with a counterweight at the other end, is used to raise water from one level to another.

terms – only in a kingdom of surpassing wealth and power could such a marvel be constructed.

Writing in the first century BC, the Greek geographer Strabo described the gardens as consisting of 'vaulted terraces raised one above the other, and resting upon cube-shaped pillars. These are hollow and filled with earth to allow trees of the largest size to be planted. The pillars, the vaults, and the terraces are constructed of baked brick and asphalt.' Asphalt (bitumen) occurs naturally in Mesopotamia, bubbling out of the ground close to the ancient site of Babylon, and was used in place of mortar in many construction projects. Strabo further informs us that 'the ascent to the highest storey is by stairs, and at their side are water engines, by means of which persons, appointed expressly for the purpose, are continually employed in raising water from the Euphrates into the garden.' Diodorus Siculus gives additional information, recording that the baked-brick walls and arches (which crumbled in wet conditions) were protected from the water by huge sheets of lead.

But what water engines could have been used to raise enough water to the highest terraces? There are three main possibilities. The simplest was the shaduf, a bucket hung from the end of a pivoted beam with a counterweight at the other end.

The second possibility is a water-screw, generally called the Archimedes screw after the Greek who is often credited with the invention. It turns inside a tube that just fits round it, and pulls water up the tube.

Finally, there is a bucket-and-chain or 'chain-pump' system, where an endless chain runs round two large wheels set one above the other. Buckets hang from it, and as the wheels are turned, the bucket at the lowest point of the lower wheel fills with water from a pool, and is carried to the highest point on the upper wheel where it empties into a second pool before returning to the bottom to be refilled.

The most primitive system, the shaduf, was surprisingly efficient – although slower than the high-tech systems – but the 'footprint' of pools and shadufs that would have been required may have been too great for the size of the hanging gardens, and many experts believe Queen Amyitis's artificial green mountain is more likely to have been watered using the more compact bucket-and-chain ensemble.

Agricultural techniques

These methods of water management were not invented specifically for the Hanging Gardens of Babylon; the people of Mesopotamia had been controlling water to grow their crops for centuries, and had developed irrigation into a fine art. Without this skill, the dry plains of the region would have remained barren. But once water could be moved easily to where it was required, the Sumerians, and later the Babylonians, developed agricultural techniques that turned Mesopotamia into the breadbasket of the world.

Mesopotamians cultivated a huge assortment of crops: barley, wheat, pulses such as lentils, beans and peas, and a wide range of vegetables, including several types of onion. They grew flax, probably for fibre rather than oil, and in the latter half of the third millennium BC they cultivated sesame (an Indian import), which gave them a form of intensive agriculture. The main cereals and pulses were winter crops, but sesame could be grown during the summer. So, with an abundant water supply, a farmer could produce two crops per year without having to bring new land into cultivation.

Probably the most important technological development was the plough, drawn by a pair of oxen. It was not the coulter, plough and turning board assembly that tamed the heavy wet soil of northern Europe. The Sumerians and Babylonians used the ard or sliding plough, which had a single pointed blade and merely broke up the surface of the ground. This was primitive, but exactly what Mesopotamian conditions required. Deep ploughing would cause irreversible damage to the soil, whereas loosening just the upper 15–20 mm (½–¾ in) gave the seedlings' roots a chance to flourish.

Just as important, this technique breaks the capillary network through which soil moisture is lost to the air by evaporation. Ard ploughing with oxen is ideal in these arid conditions: it has been shown that, compared to human tillage alone, ploughing can increase productivity by 400 per cent.

The Sumerians were responsible for another innovation: the seeder plough, which made sowing far more efficient. Jethro Tull invented a similar device in England 4000 years later, in 1701. And in about 1500 BC the Sumerians even produced an agricultural handbook, *The Farmer's Instructions*, which gives (lines 46–54) detailed advice on using this new technology:

> *On each* nindan [6 metres] *draw eight furrows; closely ranged furrows strangle the barley plants. When you seed-plough the field keep an eye on your man who drops the seed, let him drop the barley-goddess* [one barley seed] *each 2 'fingers'. Have him drop 1* gin [= 15 ml/0.5 fl oz] *to each* nindan. *If the seed does not penetrate into the womb* [of the earth] *replace the peg of the tongue of your plough.*

The Sumerians and Babylonians used ard ploughs drawn by oxen to loosen the surface of the soil. Later they invented the seeder plough, which laid seeds directly in the furrows and covered them over.

The seeder plough was labour-intensive. It required three men to work on each team: one to steer, one to turn the oxen and a third to drop the seed into the seeder. But labour was not a limiting factor in Sumer or Babylon, and the plough's efficiency more than made up for this minor drawback. It was undoubtedly the main factor in the high productivity attained by farmers in the region – possibly as high as a 30-fold increase in yield for some crops. The Sumerians needed these large harvests; farming was thirsty work, and around 40 per cent of their barley harvest was used for making beer.

Bread and beer

Irrigation causes a gradual build-up of salts in the soil, which eventually reduces yields. *The Farmer's Instructions* gives clear details on how to leach the accumulated salt from the ground, but the soil always retained some salinity. As a result, the staple cereal grown in Mesopotamia was barley; wheat and other species that they attempted to grow are less salt-tolerant. At one time (in the first century BC) Mesopotamians even experimented with rice.

The barley crop was originally eaten as porridge, as biscuits (mixed with honey) and, most commonly, as flat discs of unleavened bread, which are still common to the area and are known as *khubuz*. Later the Sumerians invented ovens for baking leavened bread – beehive-shaped structures, each with a small, funnelled chimney. Loaves were fastened to the hot inside walls of the funnel, and when they were baked they fell off into the waiting hands of the baker. If he lost concentration, the bread landed in the fire – Sumerian toast!

Barley was also the basis of beer, which was drunk at least 6000 years ago. Beer (and possibly bread) was probably discovered (rather than invented) when someone left a jar of damp barley in the corner of a warm room, and came back to find it had fermented. This process of fermentation seems to have been regarded with something approaching religious awe by Mesopotamians. Beer was certainly used in medicine; one ancient recipe for treating an infected limb calls for the affected part to be washed with 'good beer and hot water'. Beer would have been much less contaminated than water, and the alcohol it contained may well have helped to disinfect the wound.

Brewing was not to be undertaken lightly. The process took place in temples and was under the control of females – the tutelary deity of beer being the goddess Ninkasi. She was said to live on Mount Sabu, which translates as 'the mountain of the tavern keeper', and the *Hymn to Ninkasi* gives a beer recipe that still works today. Other ancient Sumerian records list the extensive equipment used in brewing, and a whole host of technical terms for the various stages. However, in the early days the quality left a lot to be desired: the beer often contained a lot of lees (suspended matter). Art from the fourth millennium BC shows that the Sumerians got around this problem by drinking their beer through long tubes, the bases of which were perforated with small holes to act as a filter.

Beer was a popular drink, partly because it was alcoholic and fun – and may well have helped the farmers and labourers survive their back-breaking toil – but also because it was safe. Sanitation was almost non-existent in Mesopotamia; most water supplies were contaminated, and the incidence of water-borne diseases was high. The fermentation process and the acidity of the beer kills many pathogens. Drinking beer instead of water not only kept the Sumerians happy, it kept them alive. This has been true throughout history – and was evident during the cholera outbreak in London in 1854.

However, as in most other societies, some people insisted on drinking too much. Drunkenness was certainly a problem, and Mesopotamians had their own ways of alleviating the results of binge-drinking, some of them quite as bizarre as modern-day hangover 'cures': 'To get a drunkard sober again: give him a gazelle to hold on to, throw an uncut pistachio nut into water, sieve it and get him to drink it.'

Regulations were put in place to control alcohol consumption. This was taken so seriously that 'opening hours' are specified in another Mesopotamian innovation: the first known written code of laws.

Law and writing

King Hammurabi ruled over Babylon between 1792 and 1750 BC. He extended the frontiers of his realm, conquering Sumer to the south and thereby uniting the whole of Mesopotamia. Like most of his contemporaries, he was a ruthless and rather cruel monarch, but he is remembered for the code of laws that he had carved on a black stone slab or stele; in fact, he set up a number of these columns. Along with the regulation of drinking places, the code listed harsh punishments for many crimes, including bearing false witness, and imposed stern penalties on corrupt judges and officials. Concepts of mercy were noticeably absent; it is in Hammurabi's code that the phrase 'an eye for an eye' first appeared. The laws were probably not all his own creation, but the continuation of a traditional law system. His great innovation was to record them in writing, so that they remained unchanged and can still be read by scholars today (see plates, page 3).

Protohumans learnt millions of years ago to communicate by sound, first in grunts and then in more precise ways, finally 'digitizing' the sounds into words in order to convey warnings, instructions, messages and ideas. Stories were remembered and repeated, generation by generation, which is how there are creation myths from so many cultures. The next major step forward was the idea of writing down the information.

The Sumerians are the people we must thank for the world-altering idea of putting spoken language into written form. It is thought that this happened in about 3000 BC in what is now southern Iraq, in a city named Uruk. For the period, Uruk was enormous, perhaps 5 km (3 miles) square, and it contained a society the like of which the world had never seen, with elaborate political and religious hierarchies.

Even before this time people in southern Mesopotamia had been using simple symbols to refer to specific animals, and others to record the size of individual flocks. But a social structure as complex as Uruk's required more detailed management – especially, a comprehensive method of record-keeping that encompassed more than lists and numbers of objects.

Over the next six hundred years Sumerian scribes developed a way to depict the spoken word. They achieved this by writing signs that represented not just the idea of an object, but the pronunciation of that object's name. In other words, the signs became *phonetic* and stood for the sounds rather than for any specific thing. Signs that were originally pictographic came to represent *phonemes*, the individual sounds from which words are composed.

At first the signs, drawn on a pillow-shaped tablet of clay, were curved, and a pointed stylus was used; but the scribes soon realized that they could be written faster and more legibly if the words were built up using the end of the stylus to make wedge-shaped impressions in the clay, rather than flowing lines. The Sumerians gloried in their new-found ability and recognized its power to conquer time and distance. King Shulgi (*c.* 2100 BC) wrote:

Now I swear by the sun god Utu on this very day, and my younger brothers shall be witness of it in foreign lands where the sons of Sumer are not known...where they have no access to the written word...that I, the firstborn son, am a fashioner of words, a composer of songs, a composer of words, and they will recite my songs as heavenly writings, and that they will bow down before my words...

This cuneiform writing remained unchanged for almost three thousand years. Its power lay in the fact that it was a script, not a language. It was used throughout the centuries to record on clay the sounds of many languages: Sumerian, Akkadian, Aramaic, Hittite and others. We retain some of its conventions to this day; just like the ancient Sumerians we read from left to right, and from top to bottom, on modern versions of a clay tablet: the paper page or computer screen. Some of the letters of our alphabet can even be traced back across five thousand years. For example, the letter A is derived from an ox's head turned through 180 degrees – it slowly turned upside-down via Canaanite and other scripts.

Recording the heavens

One thing for which Mesopotamians used their writing was to keep a record of what was happening in the heavens. This was a relatively late development, beginning in the third millennium BC, during the reign of King Ammi-saduqa of Babylon's First Dynasty, with observations on the rising and setting of the planet Venus, always near the sun. In the first millennium BC, Babylonian astrologers had developed primitive astrolabes (see page 173), consisting of three concentric circles inscribed on a tablet of clay, with 12 radii dividing the circles into 12 equal arcs. Each arc was divided in three, and in each of the 36 divisions that resulted the name of a constellation was inscribed, together with several digits. No one is really sure of the purpose of these astrolabes, but they seem to be attempts at mapping the sky, and as such are probably astronomical observations that led to another Babylonian first: the invention of the Zodiac.

The zodiacal belt is a strip of sky 12 degrees wide, within which the sun, moon and all the visible planets of our solar system move across the heavens. Also lying within this narrow strip are a number of stars, which the Babylonians grouped into the zodiacal constellations – the 'star signs' so beloved of tabloid astrology. An ancient Babylonian stargazer viewing modern horoscopes would have no difficulty in recognizing their names. Most of the constellations are identical to the Babylonian originals: the Bull, the Twins, the Lion, the Scorpion, the Archer and Capricorn are all taken directly from them.

Then as now, the people of the land between the rivers used astrology as a way of predicting the future. Horoscopes were cast for individuals, some as soon as they were born. A cuneiform text for a child born in 263 BC begins:

In the year 48 Adar the child was born. At that time the sun was in 13:30° Aries, the moon was in 10° Aquarius, Jupiter at the beginning of Leo, Venus with the Sun, Mercury with the Sun, Saturn in Cancer, Mars at the end of Cancer…He will be lacking in wealth… His food will not satisfy his hunger. The wealth which he has in his youth will not remain…

Pretty depressing stuff for a young child to grow up hearing. One wonders how he coped. The Babylonians took predictions and

The zodiac signs in use today are thought to have derived from the ancient Babylonians. Clockwise from the top: Taurus, Gemini, Cancer, Leo, Virgo, Libra, Scorpio, Sagittarius, Capricorn, Aquarius, Pisces and Aries.

omens seriously, seeing them unquestionably as messages from the gods. They studied natural phenomena like rain, hail, thunder and earthquakes; they observed the flight of birds, the swimming of fishes, how smoke rose from the fire and the contents of livers from animals sacrificed to the gods. They analysed dreams, and even had a system that divined the will of a god from the manner in which molten iron exploded when dropped into a bucket of water balanced on the head of the person who was seeking guidance from a god.

All in all, perhaps the simple stargazing of astrology was not so bad. Its predictions may have been gibberish, but it did recognize the majesty of the night sky, and the insignificance of human beings in the face of the grandeur of the universe. And it led, ultimately, to a more exact exploration of the heavens: the science of astronomy.

Inventing the wheel

It is hard to imagine civilization without the wheel, and yet the Aztecs, Mayas and Incas all managed to achieve advanced societies – with huge cities, temples, irrigation and advanced mathematics and astronomy – without the benefit of a single vehicle with wheels. Wheeled children's toys were known, but anything larger was useless on the steep and rocky trails of the Americas. The ancient Egyptians also had wheels, but gave up using them for a thousand years because it was more effective to use boats on the Nile or camels in the desert. Nevertheless, when it comes to transportation where there are smooth roads, there is no doubt that the wheel is hard to beat.

The first evidence for the use of wheeled transportation comes from the home of writing, the Sumerian city of Uruk in southern Mesopotamia. Pictograms from around 3200 BC to 3100 BC show that the technology seems to be derived from simple sledges to which four primitive wheels were fitted. No one is quite sure how the concept of the wheel originated; it may have developed from wooden rollers, which were certainly used at the time to move heavy objects, or it may be derived from some lateral thinking involving the potter's wheel – the idea is that a particularly bright potter had a '*eureka* moment' when he considered the possibilities inherent in laying his wheel on its rim.

All the early vehicles were four-wheelers pulled by paired oxen. Neither horse-drawn ones nor two-wheeled carts were pictured at this time, and both seem to have been later developments. The four-wheeled 'sledge carts' were invariably shown with a roofed super-structure, probably as protection against sun and rain. They may have been used as wheeled palanquins to transport royalty, or per-haps images of the gods, from place to place.

At first the cart's axle and wheel were built as a single unit, and revolved together under the floor of the vehicle. This arrangement works well only for slow-moving transport, however, and 'naved' wheels were gradually introduced, with the axle fastened firmly to the body of the cart while the wheels revolved on the axle, held in place by a linchpin. The main advantage of this innovation was that it allows differential rates of revolution for wheels on each side of the vehicle, making it easier to turn at speed.

Over the next eight hundred years (the Early Dynastic period) both four-wheeled and two-wheeled transportation proliferated, and the technology became incorporated into all aspects of Mesopotamian society. It becomes especially prominent in the 'battle carts' of the mili-tary – the armoured personnel carriers of their day. Long and narrow, with four wheels, they were pulled by onagers (asses) and carried a driver and a warrior. The carts were high-fronted, apparently for pro-tection against weapons thrown by the enemy, and were equipped with a large 'quiver' holding a quantity of spears that the warrior could launch at the foe. For an enemy unused to wheeled vehicles, the battle carts must have had the same effect as modern-day heavy armour attacking unsupported infantry. They would have been unstoppable.

A professional army

Mesopotamia was not really a unified country; rather, it was made up of various city states scattered through the region. These were continually vying for power and advantage, with the result that a state of almost continuous war existed between them. So engineers were always looking for military innovation. The Sumerians are credited with the invention of the metal helmet, the sickle sword, armoured cloaks and the bronze socket axe. The axe, especially, was a formidable weapon; the socket allowed a much stronger attachment of the blade to the shaft, and the Sumerians designed the axe head with a narrowing blade so that it could more easily penetrate the enemy's armour. No society in the Bronze Age was more advanced in the design and application of military weaponry and techniques.

The Sumerians also invented the idea of a standing, professional army. The tablets of Shuruppak (*c.* 2600 BC) record that the king provided for the maintenance and equipping of about seven hundred warriors, who functioned as a bodyguard and the nucleus of his army. Thanks to the Sumerian habit of recording everything they did in writing or in stone carvings, quite a bit is known about their military capabilities. The first battles for which there is detailed evidence are those between Eannatum, king of the city state of Lagash, and the king of Umma, in 2525 BC. Eannatum was victorious and set up a victory stele, the Stele of the Vultures, to commemorate his victory. This is the first pictorial monument to any war. Its images show that the Sumerian troops fought in phalanx formation, six men deep and eight wide. The phalanx implies great discipline, and reveals that the soldiers cannot have been untrained conscripts, or (as was usual in Neolithic times) a temporary aggregation of men brought together to face a crisis. This was a well-practised, highly regimented, professional force.

Some two hundred years after Eannatum the city state of Umma, led by King Lugalzagesi, established hegemony over the whole of

Sumer – but it was not to last. Just 24 years later, the Akkadians to the north (who had emulated much of Sumerian civilization – including its military techniques – and who were gradually encroaching on their southern neighbours) destroyed Lugalzagesi's empire and, under the leadership of Sargon the Great, united the whole of Mesopotamia for the first time since 4000 BC. Recruiting widely among the Sumerians, Sargon used this combined army to build the first Mesopotamian empire, a dominion that was to last three hundred years and which, at its height, stretched from the Taurus mountains to the Persian Gulf. The professional soldiers of Sumer and Akkad had proved their worth, and founded a tradition of standing armies that has continued to the present day.

Reed boats

The Sumerians never possessed a professional navy, but this is not to say that they did not bring their inventive genius to bear on boat-building. They are known to have had wood and hide boats from the earliest times, but they excelled in the construction of another type of sea craft: the reed boat.

Such boats could easily be manufactured from the *Berdi* reeds that grew in abundance in the marshlands of Mesopotamia. When fastened together in the proper way the reeds make a solid water craft, and one that remains buoyant over an extended period of time. Reed boats are common throughout the world, from Easter Island through South America to Africa. Most, especially the larger versions, have bipod masts with square sails. They also feature an upturned prow and stern which were believed, at first, to be purely decorative additions.

However, the experience of adventurer Thor Heyerdahl (who sailed reed boats of both Sumerian and Egyptian design across the open ocean in the 1960s) proved that the upturned prow and stern were essential to the ship's integrity. On his first voyage across the

Atlantic in the reed boat *Ra*, the decision was taken to cut the rope that kept the stern in its upturned shape (another rope performed the same function for the prow). Very soon the stern began to sink and the craft showed a pronounced list to one side. Heyerdahl had to abandon ship before reaching his goal. But his expedition had proved the seaworthiness of reed boats. Their natural buoyancy, and the wash-through nature of their decks, allowed them to ride the waves as readily as a swan on a lake. On Heyerdahl's second Atlantic crossing, his boat survived unscathed and did not lose a single reed from its structure. All this has strengthened the theory that similar ships from Sumer had sailed and traded as far as Africa to the west and India in the east.

The reed boats constructed by the Sumerians may have looked something like this, with an A-frame mast and an upturned prow and stern.

Many experts have predicted that a reed boat would sink after a few weeks in the water. The Sumerians seem to have had similar worries, but they also found a solution: they began coating their craft with bitumen (asphalt). Large supplies were available in Mesopotamia, and ancient seamen were not slow to take advantage of this natural waterproofing material. This tradition is followed by makers of reed boats in the region to this day.

The first electricity?

A small earthenware jar discovered in 1938 at Khujut Rabu in Mesopotamia, and thought to be at least one, and perhaps two thousand years old, produced a furore in scientific circles. Wilhelm König, the archaeologist who discovered it, believed it was an ancient battery, but his views were pooh-poohed by the archaeological establishment, who 'knew' that such technologies never existed in ancient Mesopotamia, and held to the accepted notion that the first battery was invented in 1799 by the Italian scientist Alessandro Volta (after whom the volt is named). This thing must be a scroll-holder.

Later research has cast doubt on these certainties. Just after the Second World War, the 'Baghdad battery' was re-examined by an American, Willard F. M. Gray, at the General Electric high voltage laboratory in Pittsfield, Massachusetts. The jar was about 30 cm (12 in) high, and contained a copper cylinder some 3 cm (1 in) in diameter with an iron rod in the middle (see plates, page 3). The rod passed through an asphalt stopper in the mouth of the jar, which functioned to isolate the two metals (copper and iron) from each other. Willard Gray made a replica of the ancient artefact. When he filled this with grape juice it generated a potential of approximately half a volt. Wilhelm König seems to have been right – the jar was indeed a battery. At least two thousand years ago, someone in Mesopotamia was producing electricity.

Few now doubt the truth of this. The arguments nowadays are concerned with what this strange device could possibly have been used for. It has been suggested that the current worked as an analgesic to numb pain, just as the ancient Greeks and Romans used electric fish to relieve headache and gout, as recorded by Scribonius Largus, the court physician to the emperor Claudius, in the second century AD: 'For any sort of foot gout, when the pain comes on it is good to put a living black torpedo fish under his feet while standing on the beach, not dry but one on which the sea washes, until he feels that his whole foot and ankle are numb up to the knees.'

Another idea is that the battery was used in temples. Connected to the metal image of a god, it could have given the faithful a slight shock when they touched the statue. What better way to demonstrate the power of a particular deity?

More credible is the theory that the device was used in electroplating, where a small electric current is used to apply a thin layer of metal to an object made from a different metal. The German researcher Dr Arne Eggebrecht believes this process was used to coat silver with gold, and has shown that the Baghdad battery can perform this function. He has also made the startling suggestion that many of the so-called 'gold' artefacts from this period, housed in museums the world over, are in fact gold-plated silver.

Thank the peoples of Mesopotamia

The peoples of Mesopotamia were a remarkable lot. The Sumerians were responsible for many of the basic ideas and concepts upon which a civilized society is based, including agriculture, the city and a code of laws. They invented the wheel and the written word, and their interest in the stars and their detailed record-keeping helped to lay the foundations of science. Without their genius, human progress would have remained in the slow lane for far longer, and the world today would be a very different place.

III

THE EGYPTIANS

Egypt became a unified country in 3100 BC, when the southern warrior king Narmer marched northwards along the Nile, conquering the self-governing city states that lined the river. For almost 3000 years – until the arrival of Alexander the Great in 332 BC – Egypt remained a fiercely independent land with its own very distinctive art, religion and culture. There were times of strong government and times of weak rule, but there was never any deviation from the fundamental belief that Egypt was the best country in the world. Ancient Egypt was the superpower of its day, and its kings were respected as demigods throughout the Mediterranean world.

A solar boat

The Greek historian Herodotus wrote the first travel guide to ancient Egypt. He was struck by the importance of the Nile in everyday life. As he neatly put it: 'Egypt is the gift of the Nile.' The river allowed the first Egyptians to settle in a land that is 90 per cent desert. It gave them water to drink, to cook with and to wash in. It irrigated their fields, and provided a thick mud that could be made into pottery and bricks. The Nile was both a sewer and an unfailing supply of tasty fish. There was no need for a road network, because everyone travelled by water. There were papyrus rafts for short journeys, wooden boats for longer trips and massive barges for transporting stone blocks from the quarries. Nature made river travel very easy. As the current flowed from south to north, northward journeys required little effort from the oarsmen. The return journey was even easier. As the wind blew from north to south the sailors simply put away their oars and unfurled their sails. Simple!

This total dependence on the Nile seeped deep into the Egyptian way of thought. Their sun god did not drive a flaming chariot; he sailed a solar boat that crossed the clear blue sky by day and sailed through the dark underworld at night. The dead were taken for burial across the Nile in a boat, and so boats became linked both with funerals and the sun. When King Khufu (Cheops to the Greeks) built his magnificent pyramid complex in 2551 BC he thought it essential to include them in his plans.

A felucca, with its distinctively-shaped sail. Egypt relies on the Nile for transport, as well as for irrigation and fish.

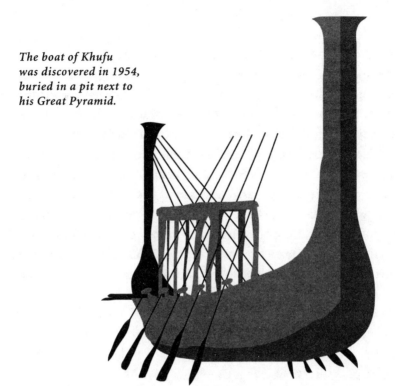

*The boat of Khufu
was discovered in 1954,
buried in a pit next to
his Great Pyramid.*

Archaeologists long ago found three boat-shaped pits associated with Khufu's pyramid, but they were disappointingly empty. Two narrow, rectangular pits lying to the south of the pyramid were a different matter. They were roofed with massive limestone slabs held in place with ancient mortar. A scribbled name on one of the slabs showed it had been lowered into place by workmen employed by King Djedefre. As Khufu's son and successor, Djedefre would have been responsible for burying his father. Both pits held disman-tled wooden boats. One of these remains where it was found and is the subject of a long-term conservation project. The other has been restored, and is now displayed in a state-of-the-art glass museum next to the Great Pyramid.

The boat was 43 metres long and almost 6 metres wide. Why, then, was it stored in a pit only 31 metres long and 2.6 metres wide? Khufu's workmen were the most experienced builders in the ancient world; they would have been quite capable of digging a pit of the right size had they so wished. The decision to bury the boat in pieces must have been a deliberate one. The excavated pit yielded 651 boat parts – an amazing 1224 pieces of wood plus rope – that had been carefully stored in 13 layers. The wood was almost perfectly preserved, and still smelled faintly of cedar.

Faced with this gigantic 3-D jigsaw puzzle, restorer Hag Ahmed Youssef spent almost 28 years reassembling the boat. He was helped in his work by the marks left on the wood by the ancient carpenters. The end result is a full-sized wooden copy of a papyrus-reed boat, which lacks a keel but has a splendidly decorative papyrus-shaped prow and an equally splendid stern socketed directly on to the hull timbers. The boat is made of cedar planks whose bevelled edges are held together with wooden pegs and then sewn together with fibre ropes that pass through channels carved in the inner surfaces of the planks, so that the stitching – a simple over-and-under stitch that goes across rather than along the hull – is invisible from outside the boat. Thin, hemispherical battens lashed over the seams may have made caulking with reeds unnecessary. The hull is strengthened by 16 frames that support the stanchions carrying the central stringer. On deck there is an enclosed cabin, a central canopy with five cere-monial oars on either side and a foredeck canopy. Two steering oars were operated from the stern.

Not one metal nail was used in the boat. This may sound a bit dangerous – don't boats that are sewn together leak? – but the ancient builders knew exactly what they were doing. When the boat entered the water the wooden planks would swell, the ropes would tighten and it would become watertight. But did it ever enter the water? Experts are divided. Some believe it is the actual funeral boat used to transport the king's body on his last journey to his pyramid. Others think it was a ritual artefact built for immediate dismantling and burial, perhaps ready for him to sail into the afterlife.

Papyrus and 'paper'

Among the Nile's important gifts to Egypt was a tall reed topped by a wide, feathery 'umbrella', that grew along its marshy banks (see plates, page 7). Papyrus was an incredibly useful plant whose long, strong fibres could be used in basketry, sandal-, rope- and boat-making; whose root could be roasted and eaten or burned as a fuel; whose flowers could be offered to the gods; and whose stalks could be shaken like a rattle in appreciation of Hathor, goddess of motherhood, drunkenness and sexuality. But the best-known use of papyrus is in the manufacture of Egyptian 'paper'.

Writing had developed at about the time Narmer marched with his troops to conquer northern Egypt. The unified land needed a strong civil service, and the ability to keep accurate records became crucial to the running of the state. Scribes – those who could read, write and count – would always be respected in Egypt. The first Egyptian writings used hieroglyphs; a non-alphabetic script made up of hundreds of signs arranged in rows or columns, and read from either left to right or right to left. They were lovely to look at, but fiddly to write, and civil servants were finding it difficult to keep up with the ever-increasing paperwork.

Five hundred years later the hieratic script – an abbreviated version of hieroglyphs that is always read from right to left – developed. Religious and royal inscriptions continued to be carved in hieroglyphs, but from this time on hieratic became the script for everyday matters.

Hieroglyphic text remained an enigma until 1822, when Jean-François Champollion managed to decipher the Rosetta Stone. This had been found by French soldiers in the small town of Rosetta, and had a carved inscription carved in three different scripts. The single message – in praise of a pharaoh – was in hieroglyphs, in demotic (the common form of Egyptian writing at the time) and in Greek. The Rosetta Stone turned out to have been carved in 196 BC, and is now in the British Museum (see plates, page 6).

The Egyptians had a limited choice of writing materials. The very rich could carve inscriptions into the stone walls of their temples and tombs. The very poor could use paints and pigments to write on limestone flakes or broken pieces of pot (the writings are called *ostraca*). The preferred writing medium was, however, papyrus paper. Unfortunately, exactly how the paper was made is unknown so we have to rely on modern experiments. These show that papyrus manufacture is a simple but time-consuming process. So, how is it done?

1. *The papyrus plant (see plates, page 7) has a triangular stalk covered in a fibrous green 'bark'; this has to be peeled away.*
2. *The stalk itself is cut or peeled (like potatoes are peeled) into thin strips and these are soaked in water.*
3. *The moist strips are placed on a linen-covered board, side by side with a very slight overlap.*
4. *A second layer of strips is placed over the first layer, but at right angles to it.*
5. *The layers are covered with linen, and then pressed or pounded. There is no need to add glue; the two layers will bond together to form a tough paper.*
6. *The sheets are dried in the sun, and then stuck together with flour-and-water glue to make one long papyrus roll.*

Fortunately, papyrus survives well in Egypt's hot, dry conditions, and today there is a wonderful library of Egyptian texts. They include a selection of true-life adventures – how Ramesses II 'the Great' defeated his enemies at the battle of Kadesh, or how Tuthmosis III fought the epic battle of Megiddo – fantasy stories of lost sailors and talking crocodiles, or textbooks and medical recipes. The medical texts are particularly intriguing as they reveal the interesting combination of practical skill and religious ritual that went into Egyptian medicine. The Edwin Smith Medical Papyrus is a very down-to-earth training manual for healers: 'If you examine a man with a split cheek, and find swelling with a raised red edge to the cut…bandage it with fresh meat. Leave the meat in place until the swelling goes down, and then treat the cut with grease and honey, applying a clean bandage every day until the cut heals.'

The instruction to sit a woman on a garlic clove and then sniff her breath to test whether she is capable of becoming pregnant is perhaps less helpful to would-be parents.

The ancient Egyptians used hieroglyphs to record their ideas in a form that was partly pictographic and partly phonetic. The hieroglyphs were eventually deciphered from the inscription on the Rosetta Stone (see page 53 and plates, page 6).

Glass and faience

Most Egyptians kept their lotions and potions in carved stone pots. Glass, which was manufactured in Egypt from 1340 BC onwards, was far too expensive for everyday use, and only royalty and the gods in the temples had access to delicate glass vessels. Earlier glass products found in Egypt, mainly beads and scarabs, were probably imported from Mesopotamia, and it may be that the first Egyptian glassworkers were prisoners of war brought back from the eastern battlefields to work on glass ingots captured as post-battle booty.

The earliest glass factory in Egypt has been found at Amarna, capital city of the heretic pharaoh Akhenaten and his beautiful wife Nefertiti. Here, alongside his sun temples and royal palaces, Akhenaten established a thriving crafts centre. His glassworkers were able to produce exquisite glass vessels without blowing the glass. Egyptologists have been able to replicate this ancient manufacturing process – a form of moulding known as core forming – and now have a good idea of how the Amarna vessels were made.

The craftsman started by moulding a pot-shaped mixture of sand and dung on the end of a solid metal rod. This core was heated, and then either dipped into molten glass or, more usually, rolled in ground glass until it was completely covered and several glass layers had built up. Bands of decorative coloured glass, or even handles, might be added at this stage. After a lengthy period of slow cooling known as annealing – essential so that the glass vessel did not explode – the finished pot was twisted off the metal rod, and the mud-and-dung core was broken up and removed.

At Amarna the glassworkers toiled next door to the craftsmen who worked with faience. This is a ceramic material made from ground-up quartzite or sand with a dash of lime and ash, and covered in a highly distinctive blue-green glaze. Its manufacture is a far older technology than glass-making, and faience beads and amulets were being made long before Narmer was born. By the time of the first pyramid (Djoser's step pyramid at Sakkara, built in 2630 BC), faience was being mass-produced. Djoser's craftsmen were confident enough to decorate his underground chambers with approximately 36,000 deep blue-green wall tiles.

Faience was used extensively in the manufacture of beads, amulets and scarabs. The Egyptians, men, women and children, loved their bright jewellery. Jewellers had no access to the precious gems that are coveted today (diamonds, sapphires, rubies, etc.) and relied instead on gold plus a wide variety of colourful semi-precious stones including amethyst, cornelian, garnet and lapis lazuli, plus blue-green faience. Beads were desirable but, as each one had to have a small hole bored through the middle for threading, they were time consuming to make and therefore expensive.

The technology of the drill used for beads is closely related to that of the fire-drill – a wooden stick that was placed in a small notch in a block of wood, then twizzled between the palms to generate heat and eventually make fire. The earliest drills followed this pattern and were simple wooden stocks with flint bits, but soon after came copper drill-bits. These, dating to the prehistoric period, were used together with a sand abrasive and were effective but slow.

The Old Kingdom tomb of Ty (5th Dynasty, 2465–2323 BC) shows the first scene involving the use of the far faster bow-drill. The long, thin bit was attached to a stock as before, but the stock was topped by a small stone cap or cup filled with grease. A carpenter would push down on the cup while a colleague 'played' the bow, the string of which was wound around the stock. Bows were made from naturally bent branches, and the longer they were, the more efficient the drill. Six tombs in the elite Theban cemetery are decorated with bead-drilling scenes and one of these, in the tomb of the vizier Rekhmire, shows three drills being operated at the same time. In other words, the craftsperson could drill three beads simultaneously – which may well have been the first-ever example of mass production. Unfortunately, none of the drills has survived.

Wigs, clothing and make-up

Colourful jewellery put the final touches to the Egyptian toilette. Members of the upper classes put a huge emphasis on personal hygiene. They scrubbed their bodies in baths and showers, then dowsed them with perfume to mask any residual smell, cleaned their teeth with twigs, chewed incense balls to freshen the breath and removed vast quantities of body hair. No respectable woman would be buried without her own razor-and-tweezers set – the scary thing is Egyptians often removed the hair from their heads too, preferring to feel the cool breeze on their naked scalp. If a more formal occasion demanded hair, they simply popped a wig on.

Men and women wore wigs, which gradually became longer and more elaborate as Egypt's dynastic age progressed. The styles for these, and for hair, changed far faster than fashions in either clothing or jewellery, and at all times men sported by far the more fancy coiffures. The worst wigs were made from coarse, red palm fibres and must have looked dreadful. The best ones, and hairpieces, were made from human hair woven or knotted on to a net, also made from human hair, and looked entirely natural. Where the hair used in wig-manufacture came from is unknown.

Wig-makers started their work by washing the hair and combing it thoroughly to remove all traces of lice and their eggs. It was then styled into braids, ringlets or whatever, and each piece was set with a light coating of wax. Finally, the semi-rigid wig or hairpiece was attached to a net of hair stretched over a head-shaped block. A final light spray of wax ensured that everything stayed in place.

Tomb scenes show party-loving Egyptians topping their wigs with 'party cones' – pale mounds of fat or wax perched on top of their heads. For a long time Egyptologists believed that these were indeed perfumed lumps of fat designed to melt as the party progressed, allowing a refreshing trickle of moist wax to roll gently down the wearer's head and face. However, this seems highly unlikely. Leaving aside the dubious desirability of having molten lard drip on to precious wigs and clothing, it is improbable that the refrigerator-less Egyptians could develop a fat or wax that would be solid at the start of the evening and melt slowly towards the end. Certainly modern experiments have failed to reproduce this effect. Many Egyptologists now think it more likely that the 'party cones' were perhaps a symbolic representation of perfume, enjoyment or even sexuality.

Make-up was an important part of everyday grooming. Both men and women wore heavy 1960s style kohl or eye-paint, applied to the upper and lower lids so that it defined and exaggerated the length of the eyes and eyebrows – think Elizabeth Taylor in *Cleopatra*. Other cosmetics were few and far between, although some women used rouge made from red ochre (iron oxide). Lipsticks and lip-glosses were rare. The eye-paints were made from ground minerals, and were available in two colours – dark grey came from galena, and green from malachite. Fashionable ladies used both colours, green on the brows and at the corners of their eyes, and grey on their lashes. Not only was this considered highly attractive, the paints were also believed to have healing and protective powers.

Women and men in ancient Egypt wore heavy eye make-up, wigs and jewellery. This woman is wearing an usekh collar made from hundreds of tiny glass beads.

Scenes in tombs invariably show upper-class Egyptians dressed in gleaming white linen. We mustn't take these scenes too seriously – many of the sheath dresses shown are so tight that, in a Lycra-less age, their wearers would have been unable to walk, bend over or sit down – but we do know that almost all clothing was made from linen and, as it is not easy to dye, the majority of the clothes were plain white.

Linen is a product of flax, a useful crop that also yields linseed oil, and in Egypt it was farmed alongside grain. At harvest time it was pulled (never cut) from the fields, then tied into bundles and rotted in slow-running water, a process that removed the tough outer stalk. After a vigorous beating with a wooden mallet, and combing between two sticks, the still-damp flax fibres were ready to spin. The Egyptians used simple hand-held spindles, and there are lots of tomb scenes showing men and women making flax thread.

After spinning came weaving. The horizontal or ground loom, a simple frame made from four pegs hammered into the ground plus two crossbars, was used from prehistoric times onwards. The more complicated vertical or fixed two-beam loom was a later development. Both types were used to produce a variety of linens, the finest of which were made in royal and temple workshops.

The Egyptians were not particularly interested in sewing, and many of their clothes are draped and tied rather then sewn. They did, however, like elaborate pleats, which are thought to have been produced by crimping the fabric between grooved boards. Pleats were a privilege of the rich who could afford to have servants re-pleat their garments every time they were washed. The poorer members of society wore simple loincloths and jellabas similar to the garments worn in rural Egypt today.

Mummification and mummies

Egypt had an almost insatiable demand for linen. Not for clothes, but for the bandages used in their funerary rituals. It is almost impossible to think about ancient Egypt without thinking about mummification – the process of artificially preserving a dead body. The belief in a life after death is widespread. But the Egyptians had a complicated theology. They believed the survival of the soul was dependent upon the survival of the body. This led to many years of messy experimentation until their undertakers discovered the best means of achieving a perfectly preserved corpse (see plates, page 7).

Egypt already had some natural mummies. In the earliest graves the dead were buried in shallow pits in the hot desert. The corpses lay curled on their sides, covered with sheets or matting. Nothing separated the body from the sand and so, as decomposition set in, body fluids drained away. Corpses dried quickly and naturally with their internal organs intact, and hair and nails in place. Eventually, the elite decided they were not happy with simple desert burials. They wanted coffins and tombs with proper walls, roofs and floors, and plenty of space for grave goods. Of course, as soon as the bodies lost direct contact with the sand they started to rot.

The earliest attempts at mummification involved padding the corpse to give it a realistic shape, then wrapping it in tight layers of bandages. Inevitably, decay set in underneath the bandages. Undertakers realized that they had to remove the internal organs and somehow dry the flesh if they wanted the body to last. This was not a difficult concept – it was one that Egypt's cooks had been applying to food storage for centuries. So the undertakers started to cut open the abdomen and pull out the organs. These could not be thrown away as they would be needed in the afterlife. There was, however, no reason why they should not be stored separately, and special containers known as canopic jars were developed to hold them.

After 15 centuries of experimentation, undertakers developed a technology that would work every time. However, they wanted to maintain their valuable monopoly and so never wrote their methods down. So how can the making of a human mummy be reconstructed? Experimentation is not really an option – we have to rely instead on the scientific examination of unwrapped mummies, plus a description left by that tireless tourist Herodotus. The one thing people today can never fully understand is the religious aspect of mummification. Undertakers were both priests and technicians, and prayers that would guarantee the deceased eternal life always accompanied their practical duties.

The first stage was the removal of the brain. A small chisel, shoved up a nostril, broke the ethmoid bone at the top of the nose. This allowed the undertaker to insert an iron hook or long-handled spoon and scoop out the grey matter. Next the skull was filled with water to encourage decomposition. The head was propped up, and the remains of the brain trickled out through the nose.

The abdomen then had to be emptied. A vertical cut was made on the left side with an obsidian knife. The contents, apart from the kidneys, were extracted, cleaned and stored. Then the diaphragm was cut and the lungs taken out. The heart, though, was left in place as it would be needed in the afterlife.

As the skin would shrink during drying, finger- and toenails were tied on with thread. The corpse was then washed, packed with temporary stuffing material and placed on a sloping board. Finally, it was covered with powdered natron salt. Natron, a mixture of sodium carbonate and sodium bicarbonate, came from the shores of the lakes in the Wadi en-Natrun in the western desert. It dehydrated the corpse and so preserved it in the same way that salting preserves beef and fish.

Forty days later the drying was complete. The body, now much lighter in weight, was emptied of its temporary stuffing and washed, dried and rubbed with oils. The abdomen was packed with linen, bags of sawdust or even dried lichen, and loosely stitched together. The arms, legs and face were packed with sawdust, fat or even mud, pushed through a series of cuts to lie between the skin and the underlying tissue. The undertakers had to be careful here – too much stuffing might cause the corpse to burst. Finally, the body was wrapped. This was a time-consuming business that took 10 or more days and used a vast quantity of cloth, but it could not be hurried as the neat, tight bandages literally held the body together. The entire process, from death to mummy, took 70 days.

The Egyptians also mummified animals, for various reasons. Some pets were given full funerals – the mummies of cats and dogs have been found at several archaeological sites, and Amenhotep II even built a pet cemetery close to his own tomb in the Valley of the Kings. Here he buried a dog, five monkeys, a baboon, three ducks and an ibis. Most of the animals that were mummified were sacred, symbolizing particular gods. A wide range of these mummies has been found, increasing in size from fish and mice to snakes, crocodiles and full-grown bulls. Finally, the Egyptians mummified cooked animals. Joints of meat were wrapped and included in tombs so that the dead would never go hungry.

The first lock?

Mummies were buried in tombs surrounded by magnificent treasures. Everyone knew this, and so security became a matter of great importance. Some kings attempted to fool robbers by including blind passageways and sliding trapdoors in their pyramids. Others, realizing that the pyramid itself was acting as a signpost to untold riches, were buried in secret rock-cut tombs hidden away in the Valley of the Kings. Here the doors were sealed but never locked; the dead kings relied on priests, security guards and magic spells to protect their bodies and their property. This misplaced trust in human nature explains why only one king, Tutankhamun, has been recovered in a substantially intact tomb – he was lucky, the entrance to his burial chamber was accidentally hidden beneath a rubbish heap.

The Egyptians used simple bolts to keep their doors shut. Rods of metal or wood, these were slid through hoops attached either to the door and door frame or, more usually, to two wooden doors. If need be they could be sealed so that, while the bolt would offer little resistance to a burglar, any unauthorized tampering would be immediately obvious.

In 1887 Sir Flinders Petrie was excavating at the workmen's village of Kahun, also known as el-Lahun. Here had lived the workmen and officials involved in the building of the nearby pyramid of Senwosret II (1897–78 BC). Petrie came across a curious object: a wooden cylinder, 23 cm (9 in) long, with perforations in its sides and with each end pierced to a depth of 1.9 cm (¾ in). He had no idea what it could be, but similar pieces of wood were occasionally recovered from other sites, including one that turned up as part of the toilette set of Merit, wife of the architect Kha. As these cylinders were associated with women, it was first believed that they were a form of obscure beauty aid – perhaps a hair-curling wand? Then, in 1907, similar wooden cylinders were seen in use as keys in Ethiopia. Had Petrie in fact found the world's first security system?

How could the key have worked? This is fiendishly complicated to describe, but the key itself is relatively simple if fiddly to use. The only trouble is, it is not exactly crime-proof. Anyone equipped with a suitable sized wooden cylinder and a piece of string could open the door. First imagine a simple, wooden bolt system on the inside of an inward-opening door. The bolt has a piece of string attached to the end facing the direction of slide (in best scientific tradition, we will call this string A). String A passes through a keyhole in the door; by pulling hard on the string it is possible to draw the bolt home and effectively lock the door on the inside. String A, still attached to the bolt is, of course, left dangling outside the door.

To open our locked door we need a key that will push back the bolt. As the Greeks later discovered, this could be done in a relatively simple way by inserting a rigid metal key resembling a crocheting hook through the keyhole, hooking it into a notch in the bolt, and pushing. Our key, however, is a cylindrical piece of wood with a piercing at one end and its own piece of string attached at the other (string B). It is going to knock the bolt back into place.

LEFT *The Bronze Age was a time of ostentatious personal adornment – for the few who could afford it. Torcs, like this highly decorated example, were worn around the neck, and are often associated with Celtic warriors.*

BELOW *The ruins of Skara Brae were discovered in 1850 when a storm hit the Orkney islands, tearing the turf from the sand dunes. As well as their stone cupboards, beds, hearths and shelves, this group of late-Neolithic dwellings retain their lavatories, with drains leading outside – possibly the oldest lavatories in the world.*

The Egyptians

LEFT *An unusual view of the three Giza pyramids with the Cairo suburbs and the edge of the Giza plateau in the foreground. The Great Pyramid, at the right in this picture, is the oldest of the Seven Wonders of the World and the only one still standing. It was built for Khufu (known to the Greeks as Cheops), the second king of the 4th Dynasty, who died around 2528 BC. Built from about 2.3 million stone blocks, it stands 146 metres high, and the sides, each 230 metres long, are lined up precisely north–south and east–west.*

BELOW *Ancient Egyptian tombs were often decorated with images of food, drink and other things that the deceased person might need in the afterlife. This incredibly fresh and lifelike painting of geese forms part of a frieze found in the* mastaba *(burial chamber) of Princess Itet at Meidum in Lower Egypt, and is about 4630 years old.*

ABOVE *The Rosetta Stone, held in the British Museum since 1802, is part of a black basalt stele that dates from the third century AD. It was found near Alexandria at the time of the French occupation of Egypt in 1799 and provided the key to deciphering ancient Egyptian hieroglyphs (which appear at the top), as it included translations of the same text – a decree by Ptolemy V – in demotic script (middle) and in Greek (bottom). Jean-François Champollion became a national hero in France when he eventually cracked the hieroglyphic code in 1822.*

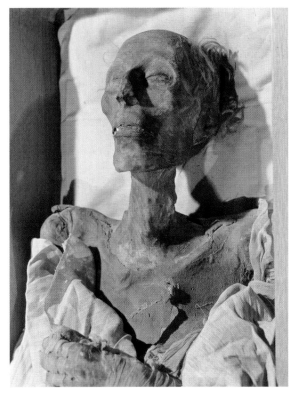

LEFT *The well-preserved mummy of Ramesses II has revealed that he lived to be over 80 (an unusually old age), walked with a limp and suffered from arthritis, abscesses on his teeth and hardening of the arteries. He died around 1212 BC and may have been the pharaoh mentioned in the book of Exodus.*

BELOW *The ancient Egyptians were skilled furniture makers. This ornate bed leg, which is decorated with a golden snake design, is about 3400 years old (18th Dynasty).*

LEFT *Papyrus growing along the banks of the Nile. The ancient Egyptians developed a way of turning the stalks of this plant into a type of paper by soaking them in water and drying them in the sun. Without papyrus, the detailed written records of their civilization would not have survived.*

The Indians

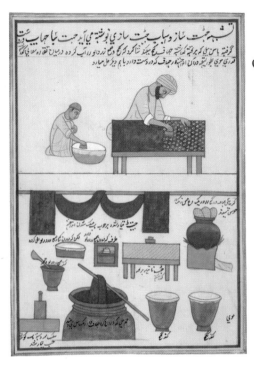

LEFT *The Indians were excellent metal workers. This dagger, with its horse-head handle, dates from the seventeenth century.*

FAR LEFT *This picture from the 1850s shows Indian craftsmen printing (top) and dyeing cotton by hand, using traditional techniques that have been passed down from each generation to the next.*

BELOW *Dyed cotton hanging out to dry in India today.*

ABOVE *The 4500-year-old ruins of Mohenjo-Daro in the Sind region of Pakistan – perhaps the first ever example of town planning.*

On string B there is a flat, wooden disc wider than the keyhole. String A is threaded through the hole in one end of the cylinder, which is then pushed through the keyhole. The flat disc on string B stops the cylinder from falling to the ground behind the locked door. String A is then pulled, raising the cylinder so that it hovers dead in line with the bolt. If string A is then held fast, and string B is jerked hard, the cylinder will bang into the bolt and push it back. Easy!

The tumbler lock, which is often called the 'Egyptian lock' and which is the forerunner of modern locks, is not an Egyptian invention at all, but was actually developed in Mesopotamia.

Technology and tools

Metal tools were used on all Egypt's building sites. They carved delicate inscriptions into the walls of the temples, and chiselled hard stone into the likenesses of kings. They were extremely valuable, and extremely well guarded. At the end of every day in the Valley of the Kings, as the workforce clocked off, the copper chisels were carefully collected and counted. They were locked away, and would not be seen again until the next morning.

Copper had been worked in Egypt since 4000 BC, when colourful copper oxide ores such as malachite and azurite were smelted at relatively low temperatures, first using simple crucibles and banks of three or more blowpipes, and later in basic pottery furnaces. But more efficient processing demanded the use of a wider range of ores, and these needed higher temperatures and the addition of 'flux', usually iron oxide, which would help the copper to melt and separate from its ore. The development of the shaft furnace met these needs, and copper production was stepped up to meet the growing demand.

The foot-operated bellows, or pot bellows, was another huge technological advance, allowing a more powerful and constant jet of air that increased the furnace temperature. As their name suggests, they were pots fitted with loose leather diaphragms tight-fitted at the rim. A long piece of string attached to the centre of the pot allowed the bellows to be pumped up and down either by hand or, more usually, by foot. None of these early bellows has survived, but tomb scenes dating to the 18th Dynasty (1550–1307 BC) show furnace-workers standing on these curious, cushion-like bellows.

The development of metallurgy, and the widespread availability of tools made first of copper then of bronze, had a huge impact on Egyptian woodworkers. Up until this point trees had been cut with stone axes hafted into wooden handles, and saws were flint knives with serrated edges. Metal allowed the development of efficient carpentry and joinery tools including saws, adzes and chisels. Egypt was a land lacking in tall trees, and all large-scale timber had to be imported from Syria and the Lebanon. Despite these handicaps it had some of the most technically advanced carpenters in the ancient world. Just think of the rich wooden furniture recovered from Tutankhamun's tomb: bed frames, headrests, thrones, stools, life-sized wooden statues, and much, much more (see plates, page 7).

Of course, other ancient civilizations had furniture too. The reason why we know so much more about carpentry in Egypt is that Egyptian furniture and tools survived in tombs, and paintings on tomb walls actually show carpenters in action. This does mean, however, that although there is a fine selection of upper-class furniture, very little is known about how ordinary people furnished their homes.

So what tools were available to Egyptian carpenters? We have already met the bow drill. Axes and adzes, used to cut down trees and split and shape the timber, and mallets formed from a single piece of wood, were very similar in design to modern tools. The curved Egyptian saw evolved from the serrated copper knife. Unlike our own saws, its teeth were all punched from one side – which meant it was difficult to use as it constantly jammed in the saw-cut.

By the late fourth century BC there are illustrations of carpenters operating wood-turning lathes. This was a two-man operation. The wood to be worked – perhaps for a stool leg – was held top and bottom in a clamp while an assistant used a piece of rope to rotate it in first one direction then another. This allowed the carpenter to work the leg with a chisel. The final sanding was done with a block of quartzite.

The most expensive Egyptian furniture was decorated either with precious inlays and veneers – ebony, ivory and faience were popular choices – or with thin sheets of silver and gold. Those who couldn't afford such splendid furniture cheated by using paint. The surface of the wood was sanded and a thin layer of plaster was applied, and the artist could then replicate expensive fine-grained timber with ebony and ivory inlays.

The Great Pyramid

Herodotus believed that Khufu, owner of the solar boat, had been a cruel tyrant who made his people suffer to build the Great Pyramid. This is almost certainly unfair. There is no contemporary evidence to suggest that Khufu oppressed his people, and recent archaeological research at Giza is allowing scholars to reassess the whole pyramid-building process.

The Great Pyramid (see plates, pages 4–5), the only surviving Wonder of the Ancient World', stands 146 metres high, with a slope of 51 degrees. Its sides, with an average length of 230 metres, vary by less than 5 cm (2 in). This vast scale leaves visitors lost for words. Higher than St Paul's Cathedral, the Statue of Liberty and the Taj Mahal, it has been calculated that its base could easily accommodate Westminster Abbey, St Paul's Cathedral, Florence cathedral, Milan cathedral and St Peter's, Rome. Napoleon Bonaparte even worked out that there is enough stone in the three Giza pyramids to build a wall 3 metres high all around France.

The pyramid was aligned with amazing accuracy to true north. There are several ways this might have been achieved. The architects may have used a false horizon – a low, circular wall built on flat ground. An observer, standing inside the circle and looking northwards, would have used a forked sight and a plumb line to note the exact positions of the rise and fall of a chosen star. By extending these points to the centre of the circle, and then bisecting the resulting angle, he would have found true north. A variant on this method involves aligning two opposed circumpolar stars, one at its upper culmination and the other at its lower, with a plumb line. Both methods would have been impractical for use during daylight, and so the builders may also have made a less accurate estimation of true north from the shadows created by the sun.

It is not known exactly how many blocks of stone were built into the pyramid, but experts have estimated upwards of 2,300,000. These varied in size from 16 tonnes to a 'mere' 3 tonnes. They were dragged to the building site on sleds – fortunately most of them came from a nearby quarry – then raised into position via ramps. It would have been impossible to have one long ramp rising to the top of the pyramid; it would have to have been many miles long and would have taken longer to build than the pyramid itself. It seems likely that a single, straight ramp was built up to a third of the pyramid's height, and that there was a smaller, wrap-round ramp that allowed the placement of the upper blocks.

Seen from the outside, the pyramid was once a perfectly smooth, shining mirror that reflected the sun's rays and was visible for miles around. Unfortunately, the high-quality white limestone that originally cased it was removed many years ago, and used in the building of medieval Cairo.

Inside the pyramid there is a system of passageways and chambers. From the entrance on the north face a tunnel drops through the masonry to enter the appropriately named Subterranean Chamber, an incomplete room of unknown purpose. Part of the way along the descending passageway is the entrance to the ascending one. This opens into the Grand Gallery, a tall corridor with walls

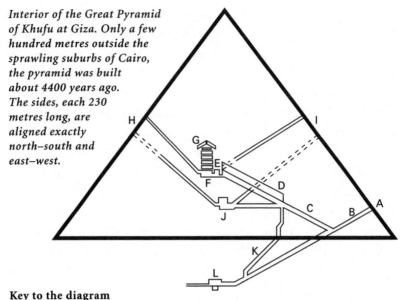

Interior of the Great Pyramid of Khufu at Giza. Only a few hundred metres outside the sprawling suburbs of Cairo, the pyramid was built about 4400 years ago. The sides, each 230 metres long, are aligned exactly north–south and east–west.

Key to the diagram
A *Entrance.* B *Descending passage.* C *Ascending passage.* D *Grand Gallery.*
E *Antechamber.* F *King's burial chamber.* G *Stress-relieving chambers.*
H *Diagonal shafts orientated towards the stars of Orion.* I *Diagonal shafts orientated towards the north pole stars.* J *'Queen's Chamber'.* K *'Well shaft'.*
L *Subterranean Chamber*

made from layers of overlapping limestone blocks. The gallery leads upwards to an antechamber, and finally to the red-granite burial chamber. Here lies Khufu's enormous, red-granite sarcophagus. The ceiling above it was built from nine granite slabs, and five stress-relieving chambers were provided directly above the burial chamber. These spread the load of the pyramid which might otherwise have put an intolerable weight on the ceiling.

The lower west wall of the gallery includes the small entrance to the 'well', a vent that drops almost to the end of the descending passageway. Here, too, is the entrance to the horizontal corridor that leads south into the so-called 'Queen's Chamber'. This room, not quite complete, is built of limestone and includes a niche that may once have housed a statue of the king.

Herodotus wrote that the pyramid was built by 100,000 slaves who 'laboured constantly and were relieved every three months by a fresh gang'. But Khufu did not have a vast body of slaves at his disposal and, even if he had, there was no way that 100,000 men could work simultaneously on the building site and quarry. It is now accepted that the pyramid was built by maybe 5000 permanent, salaried employees plus up to 20,000 temporary workers. The workers were housed in a special city just outside the cemetery wall. Here Egyptologists Mark Lehner and Zahi Hawass have discovered an industrial complex dedicated to serving the pyramid-builders. It includes a copper-processing plant, two bakeries and a fish-processing unit. Animal bones show that the workmen enjoyed a good and varied diet, including choice cuts of beef, washed down with a plentiful supply of beer. Perhaps life was not too bad on the pyramid site after all.

Thank the Egyptians

The Egyptians are not famous for their scientific inventions. We tend to think of them as traditionalists, reluctant to experiment and slow to adapt to change. But nothing could be further from the truth. If they didn't make changes to their technology, it was because they had long ago found the best solutions to their problems. They were pioneers in the fields of astronomy, agriculture, building technology and medicine, and master craftsmen skilled in the arts of mass production and man-management.

IV

THE INDIANS

Ancient Indian culture has transformed our modern lives in the most fundamental of ways. With inventions ranging from the practical (cotton clothing) through the intellectual (recognition of the 'number' zero) to the spiritual (the development of Buddhism, Hinduism and holistic healthcare), India's thinkers can take their place among the world's greatest innovators. But before we marvel at India's finest inventions, we need to understand something of her long history and culture. Here, I am using the term India to refer to the entire subcontinent, including Pakistan and Bangladesh.

The history of India is one of increasingly large town and city sites. Four and a half thousand years ago a mighty civilization already flourished along the banks of the Indus River. The people who built those cities are known today as Harappans. At its peak, Harappan civilization spread from Gujarat and the Indian Ocean to the Punjab and the Himalayan foothills, with outposts as far away as northern Afghanistan. Disturbed by the large-scale movements of Indo-European peoples from Central Asia, it came to an abrupt end around 1700 BC, and was replaced by a decentralized system of tribal, farming villages introduced by the spiritually sophisticated Indo-Aryan peoples. The Indo-Aryans were the authors of India's sacred Sanskrit texts, the Vedas.

This was just a temporary hiccup in India's unstoppable urban growth. A thousand years later, just before the birth of the Buddha (who lived *c.* 563–483 BC), Indians were once again living in cities. Alexander the Great campaigned in northwest India from 327 to 325 BC. His withdrawal left a power vacuum that was filled by the Mauryan dynasty, which lasted from the fourth to the second century BC. Under their patronage Buddhism spread throughout the Indian empire. The collapse of the Mauryan dynasty allowed local kingdoms to come to the fore. The vast Kushana kingdom dominated northern India in the first centuries AD. The Kushans were keen traders with important commercial links with Rome; their trade missions along the Silk Road introduced Buddhism to China. Finally the Gupta dynasty (fourth to sixth century AD) saw Hinduism emerge from its earlier Vedic form and spread throughout India.

Cotton and fast dyes

The classical writer Herodotus wrote about Indian cotton:

> *In India, which is the furthest region of all the inhabited world towards the east…there are trees which grow wild there, the fruit whereof is a wool exceeding in beauty and goodness that of sheep. The natives make their clothes of this tree-wool.*

Four and a half thousand years ago the people of the Indus Valley were already accomplished textile workers. Their city of Mohenjo-Daro has provided us with many examples of dyed cloth and sewing implements, while the earliest written references to Indian cotton are found in the *Rig Veda*, the oldest of the sacred Sanskrit poems of the Indo-Aryan peoples, which were composed around 1500 BC, but not written down until about 600 BC. The Indian cottonworkers were so skilful that – while we were lumbering around Britain dressed in itchy wool, heavy furs and stiff leathers – the Indians were floating about in light-as-air garments made from 'jamdani', a muslin cotton so fine that many westerners who saw it confused it with silk.

Ripe cotton bolls (seed cases) are picked from the plants when they have burst open. The seeds are removed from the fluffy white lint that surrounds them. The lint is combed into fibres which are then spun into thread.

Indian cotton was greatly admired throughout the ancient world. The Romans, in particular, could not get enough of it – they tried to make it themselves but failed, and so were forced to spend a great deal of money importing the precious stuff. By the mid-eighteenth century, India had clothed most of the globe. Its cotton fabric was lightweight, washable, available in a cheerful range of colours, and so fine it was virtually see-through – a fact much appreciated by the more daring ladies and, presumably, their gentlemen admirers. Indian cotton really did brighten up the world's wardrobe. (See plates, page 8.)

The cotton plant is a tropical and semi-tropical shrub belonging to the genus *Gossypium*. It has broad, three-sectioned leaves, and in the wild can grow up to 3 metres high. The cotton seeds are held in seed-cases known as bolls, and are surrounded by fluffy white- or cream-coloured fibres called lint. This lint is the source of the cotton cloth. The bolls are gathered when they have ripened and burst open. The lint is then separated from the seeds. This is a time-consuming business – before mechanization a pound of cotton took a whole day to de-seed. Hand-picked cotton is relatively clean, but it is usually combed, or carded, before processing. Not only does combing remove debris and align the fibres, it also eliminates the shorter, unwanted fibres.

After de-seeding and combing, the cotton is ready to be made into yarn suitable for weaving. The individual cotton fibres are only 1–2 cm long, and to turn them into a useful thread they have to be spun, which is done in two stages. First a bundle of fibres is drawn out into a long 'rope', which in the north of England is called roving. This is much thicker than cotton thread but has no strength at all; pull and it comes apart. The roving is then teased and twisted – teased out to perhaps twice its original length, and then twisted to lock the fibres together. The fibres are slightly whiskery, and twisting them together locks them into one strong thread.

The wool-spinners of Europe and the linen-spinners of dynastic Egypt used simple drop spindles. Their un-spun yarn was loosely twisted together by hand, then attached to a weighted stick (the spindle). The spindle was dropped, rolled over the thigh or other-wise emphatically twirled, to pull and twist the separate fibres into one long strand. When the yarn had been given sufficient twist it was wound around the spindle, and the process was repeated again, and again, and again, until the yarn was long enough to weave into cloth. The Europeans had a slight advantage over the Egyptians in that they used a distaff – a simple, forked stick, either held in the hand or tucked in the belt – to hold the un-spun thread, but even so hand-spinning was a tediously time-consuming business. Perhaps this was why it was traditionally done by women; the word spinster used to mean someone who spun cotton and now means an unmarried woman, while distaff means women's work, and the distaff side of the family is the female side.

The Indian spinners started out with nature on their side – their cotton fibres naturally twisted in a corkscrew fashion. Then they gained a huge technological advantage by developing the spinning wheel. The spinning wheel is basically a spindle turned on its side and connected to a drive wheel, with a pulley system added. Later a foot pedal would be added for increased efficiency. The spinning wheel mechanized the whole tedious process, halving the time needed for hand-spinning. This both saved time and gave the added benefit of a more uniform yarn, allowing the spinner to add more twist in thin places and draw out the thicker places. The spinning wheel was introduced to Europe in the Middle Ages. It remained in widespread use until the 1760s, when, in England, James Hargreaves invented the spinning jenny and Richard Arkwright invented the water frame. These two inventions took spinning out of the cottages and into the factories, rendering the spinning wheel all but obsolete. Lancashire's cotton trade had started!

Their texture was not the only thing that made Indian cottons so desirable; the colours were beautiful, and they were washable, too. There was no comparison between the dull British woad (*Isatis tinctoria*), the blue plant dye traditionally used to colour wool, and its more vibrant relation, Indian indigo (*Indigofera tinctoria*). But indigo was not easy to use. The traditional method of preparing indigo dye was to tie the cut plant into bundles, pack it into fermenting vats, and steep it in water until it fermented. The pale-coloured liquid was then drawn off and beaten with paddles until it turned blue. At this stage the indigo precipitated out of the liquid and collected as flakes on the bottom of the vat. The flakes were gathered, boiled in water, filtered, pressed, dried and cut into cubes. This solid indigo dye was insoluble in water and had to be dissolved in dilute acid before use. With the blessing of Ghata Mali, goddess of the vat, the indigo would turn a white length of cotton a beautiful blue.

The water clock

The Greek inventor Ktesibios devised ingenious water clocks in the third century BC (see page 142), but the Indians came up with a rather different gadget. By the first centuries AD they were recording time with an accurate water clock, which they called a *ghatika-yantra*. The clock itself was so simple you could easily make one at home. It consisted of a small hemispherical bowl made of copper or, in southern India, a coconut, with a small hole in its bottom. The bowl was called a *ghati*, or *ghatika*. Floated in a larger pot of water, the bowl would gradually fill with water and sink. When it reached the bottom – with an audible thud to alert the timekeeper – the process would start all over again.

If you want to make one you'll need a low plastic container (such as a shallow cottage cheese or coleslaw pot), weighted with a few coins. Carefully punch a small hole or two in the bottom with a hammer and nail. Try floating it on the water in a washing-up bowl or saucepan, and see how long it takes to sink.

The size of the hole and the weight of the *ghati* were carefully adjusted so that the bowl sank exactly 60 times in 24 hours. As there are 1440 minutes in 24 hours, the bowl took exactly 24 minutes to fill with water and sink. The Indian day and night was therefore divided into 60 periods, each 24 minutes long. These 24-minute time-periods, like the small pots, were known as *ghati*. The *ghati* could be sub-divided into 60 *palas*, each 24 seconds long. Translated into our concept of hours and minutes, this meant that an Indian 'hour' was 24 minutes long; an Indian 'minute' 24 seconds.

The water clock was used by priests to make sure that religious rituals were carried out at the correct time. By the first half of the fifth century AD the *ghatika-yantra* had become the standard equipment for measuring time in Buddhist monasteries, and the contemporary religious commentator Buddhaghosha tells us the story of the monk Kaladeva, 'Lord of Time', whose job it was to strike a bell each time the *ghati* hit the bottom of the pot. Kaladeva became so accustomed to the rhythm of his job that eventually he could strike the bell accurately without actually watching his clock. Two centuries later the water clock could be found in India's palaces as well. Announcing time had become a secular royal ritual, and the sinking of the bowl was announced by sounding bells, drums, conch shells and gongs.

Much later the British in India adopted the water clock, although some of their clocks were altered so that they recorded 60-minute hours (or 30-minute half hours) rather than Indian *ghatis*. We have a fascinating account of a traditional water clock penned by an Englishwoman married to a Muslim and living in Lucknow in the early 1800s. Mrs Meer Hassan Ali makes it clear that the water clock, once a Buddhist instrument, had by now become an integral part of upper-class Muslim households:

> *The* durwan *(gate-keeper), or the* chokeedars *(watchmen), keep the time. In most establishments, the watchmen are on guard two at a time, and are relieved at every watch, day and night. On these men devolves the care of observing the advance of time by the floating vessel, and striking the hour, in which duty they are required to be punctual, as many of the Mussalman's services of prayer are scrupulously performed at the appointed hours.*

Water clocks fell into disuse following the introduction of pendulum clocks by the Dutch scientist Christiaan Huygens in the seventeenth century, and, later, of spring clocks and watches in the eighteenth, but the newfangled mechanical devices were often less than reliable. At the end of the nineteenth century, when Rudyard Kipling's father was curator of Lahore Museum, the modern clock was out of order so often that he installed an old-fashioned water clock for the use of the policemen guarding the museum. Now obsolete except for occasional religious uses, the *ghatika-yantra* lives on in the Indian language, and many Indians still refer to their watches as *ghati*.

Bronze and the lost-wax process

Accurate timekeeping developed from the desire to perform specific religious rituals at precise times. Metallurgy, too, developed to meet religious needs. India's traditional faiths, Buddhism and Hinduism, required the creation of physical images of the Buddha and the thousands of Hindu gods. These icons played an important part in prayer and ritual and, because some of them were portable, were fundamental in spreading religious belief across the Indian peninsula. India's metalworkers made their sacred images using the lost-wax casting method.

The origins of lost-wax casting are obscure. We know it was used throughout the Bronze Age world, and it is possible that it was developed independently in different regions, at different times. The process is well suited to casting complicated shapes such as icons, and can be used to make hollow castings. Ancient the technique may be, but it is not outdated – it is still used in the West to cast intricate industrial parts, delicate jewellery and dental restorations!

Basically the craftworker fashions a wax model and encases it within a clay mould, then heats the mould so that the wax melts and can be poured out, or 'lost'. The craftworker is left with a hollow clay mould ready to receive molten metal. (More details on page 25.)

The Indian metalworkers have retained this method of working for almost four and a half thousand years, although today it is the preserve of just a handful of craftsmen. They fashion their models from a traditional mixture of beeswax, tree sap and oil, and their clay moulds are made from river sand mixed with cow dung. Bronze – an alloy, or mixture, of 90–70 per cent copper and 10–30 per cent zinc – became the favoured metal for secular lost-wax sculptures. But many religious icons were made from an alloy of five metals: copper, tin and zinc, plus traces of silver and gold. This mixture had spiritual significance: the *Shilpa Sutra*, an ancient text of Indian sculpture and iconography, maintained that the five metals stood for the five elements that made up the divine form.

Chess

Chess is a gentle, scholarly game enjoyed by schoolchildren and bespectacled academics, but it is also a game of confrontation, strategy and military tactics. The chessboard is a chequered battlefield, the pieces are soldiers and the players are generals who, with cold calculation, send their men forward to meet their fate. No board game rouses the passions more than chess. And one minor cause of argument is the origin of the game.

The Indians were keen on board games. They have provided us with some of the world's oldest sets of dice, and they developed the game of snakes and ladders, which some scholars believe reflects the Indian idea of *karma*: that every action, good or bad, has a consequence in this or the next life. The British 'discovered' snakes and ladders in India and introduced it as a children's game to Britain in the 1890s. Later it crossed the Atlantic, appearing in the United States as 'chutes and ladders' in 1943.

For many years it was accepted that chess had developed in northern India and spread throughout the world, making its way to China along the Silk Road. Recently, however, it has been suggested that chess may have evolved in China and spread westwards, to India. Experts are divided on this matter, but the oldest written evidence tends to support the theory of an Indian origin. A Persian poem dated *c.* AD 600 (the lengthily named *Karnamak-i-Arakhshatr-i-Papakan*)

The Indians loved board games and are thought to have invented chess.

includes a specific reference to a hero skilled in the game of chess. In China the first undisputed reference to chess is dated to around 800.

Over a thousand years ago the Indians were playing a war-game named *chaturanga* on a board of 64 squares, like today's chessboard. Across this board battled armies of 16 pieces – one *raja* (king), one *mantra* (vizier or counsellor, later to evolve into the modern queen), two *gaga* (elephants, later to evolve into bishops), two *asva* (horses), two *ratha* (chariots or rooks), and eight *pedanti* (soldiers or pawns). This was a four-handed game played with dice, and victory depended on the closing position of the king. From *chaturanga* there developed the two-handed Persian game of *shatranj*. In this revised game, victory was gained by capturing either the king, or all the other pieces.

By the end of the eleventh century chess was established as a game played by the aristocracy across Italy, Spain, France and Scandinavia. One nobleman, Count Ermengol of Uthell, valued his chess set so highly that he specifically bequeathed it in his will to a convent in France. The Vikings – a notoriously fierce people, not normally associated with board games – carried the game to Iceland. They were probably responsible for the Isle of Lewis chess set, which is not actually a set at all, but a collection of carved walrus-ivory chess pieces taken from several sets. These were discovered in 1831 on the south shore of Uig Bay, on the western coast of the Isle of Lewis, in the Outer Hebrides. Local peasant Calum nan Sprot had been looking for a lost cow when he stumbled across a small chamber housing over 100 small figurines. He was so frightened by the lifelike expressions on their faces that he ran straight to the local minister, Alexander McLeod. The canny McLeod exorcised the find-spot, and then sold 82 of the pieces to the British Museum for the then-princely sum of £85.

By about 1400 chess, with rules roughly as we know them today, was being played on a pan-European basis. The game had become so popular that, in 1474, William Caxton printed *The Game and Playe of the Chesse*, the second book ever to be printed in English using moveable type. Both chess rules and board design continued their slow evolution until the early nineteenth century, when the international rules of chess were established. Today chess is played around the world, including fierce battles on the internet.

Crucible steel

While the women of the late Roman empire revelled in the comfort of lightweight Indian cotton, their menfolk appreciated the hard edge of their Indian steel weapons. The Indians developed crucible steel some time before AD 300, and were soon exporting it to the rest of the world. Widely respected, Indian steel was said to slice through a man with a single stroke, or cut a piece of silk in two as it fell to the ground. If bent around a man, an Indian steel sword would apparently spring back to its original shape when released.

So what exactly was this wonder metal? Steel is an alloy of iron with a small percentage of carbon. Crucible steel is, as its name suggests, a method of making steel by heating the iron in a crucible. Indian crucible steel is widely known as wootz, a wonderful name derived from the Anglicization of *ukku* or *hookoo*, the word for steel in many southern Indian languages. An alternative name occasionally used, Damascus steel, is downright confusing – this steel was made many miles from Damascus.

Wootz was made by first mixing either wrought iron, or iron ore with charcoal, and glass. (The charcoal was there to reduce the iron ore to metallic iron – see page 104.) The mixture was sealed in a crucible, heated in a furnace and then allowed to cool, slowly. As it cooled the impurities in the steel bonded to the molten glass and floated to the surface, leaving behind 'buttons' of high-carbon steel of immense strength and flexibility.

Europeans repeatedly tried to make wootz, but failed – until 1740, when Benjamin Huntsman, a clockmaker engaged in a constant search for improved steel for his clock springs, developed an entirely new crucible process. Huntsman came from Doncaster and made clocks there, but was dissatisfied with the steel that he was able to buy; the quality was so variable that he could not make reliable springs. He moved to Sheffield, where there were better supplies of coke, and developed his method, which could produce only 25 kg (55 lb) of steel in several hours, but the steel was better than any that had been made before. This meant that Sheffield became one of Britain's foremost industrial cities, famous for its steel. In 1837 the Russian Pavel Anosov developed a third method of crucible-steel production. Finally, in 1856, Henry Bessemer invented a large-scale process that could make 30 tonnes of superb steel in half an hour, and so made crucible steel obsolete – although some say the method came from China via an American called Kelly.

Plastic surgery

One of the many uses to which the Indians put their fine steel was making sharp surgical knives. They excelled both at the manufacture of surgical instruments and at surgery itself, and their medical knowledge was equal to most in the ancient world. Indian doctors had access to a wide range of drugs, and they realized the need for light, fresh air and cleanliness – something that we in the West didn't really appreciate until the nineteenth century. Doctors were carefully trained – they practised lancing abscesses by slicing into a thin leather bag filled with slime; they practised stitching skin by sewing cloth; and they practised cauterizing pieces of meat. This training paid off. At a time when the British paid reluctant visits to the local barber for painful and inept surgery, Indian doctors understood Caesarean sections, bone-setting, cataract removals and intestinal operations.

You may have thought that plastic surgery was a recent, American invention, somehow connected with the film industry. Think again! The Indians were performing complex cosmetic surgery thousands of years before Columbus sailed west. Plastic surgery leaves little evidence for archaeologists to uncover, but we know that the ancient

Indians were going in for nose jobs because, in approximately 600 BC, the celebrated surgeon Sushruta wrote the *Sushruta Samhita*, a medical textbook that drew upon long-established oral tradition. Using a mixture of prose and poetry it includes details of surgical tools (he describes 120 medical instruments), over a thousand illnesses and injuries, and a long list of surgical procedures.

Sushruta, a pupil of the famous surgeon-king Devadas, specialized in rhinoplasty, or nose reconstruction. Noses were frequently lopped off, in accidents or battles, and by way of punishment for criminals, and Sushruta appeared to have a high success rate in reconstructing them, using flaps of skin taken from the cheek. Two centuries later, Vagbhat wrote an expanded plastic-surgery manual, the *Ashtanga Hridyans Samhita*, in which he included details of skin-grafting and organ transplants.

Surgery lost much of its high status when Buddhist scripture decreed that contact with blood and pus was polluting. High-caste doctors now turned their attention to medicine, and it was left to the manual workers such as the *koomars*, or potters, to maintain the surgical tradition. The new surgeons continued to rebuild noses, and developed a particular skill in forehead rhinoplasty, using a flap of skin taken from the forehead to restore the nose. Their 'pedicle-flap technique' left the skin graft attached to its original site by a pedicle or stalk of skin, thereby preserving its blood supply. A development of this method, which involved taking tissues from other parts of the body, was used by the surgeons of East Grinstead hospital to repair the faces of badly burned aircrew during the Second World War.

It was not until the seventeenth century, and the advent of the East India Company, that British surgeons learned the art of rhino-plasty. Europeans had tried for centuries to graft skin from healthy parts of the body to repair damaged areas. Many of their experi-mental methods were bizarrely optimistic; in one Italian scheme the surgeon strapped the patient into a specially designed jacket, cut a flap of skin on the arm, bent the arm until the flap met the damaged nose – and then expected the patient to stay with his arm in the bent position for 40 days and nights, until the skin from the arm grew over the nose. Needless to say, it didn't work!

During the nineteenth century, European doctors started to study the ancient Sanskrit texts in an attempt to understand Indian methods of nose and face restoration. The development of anaesthetics and the growing understanding of surgical hygiene (antisepsis) were a great help, making surgery virtually free from pain and infection. Two world wars brought a horrific toll of facial disfigurements, and further boosted the development of plastic surgery in both East and West.

What made the Indians such good healers? Like many ancient peoples, they had a long-held belief that science and religion were deeply linked, that there was a strong connection between the mind and the body, and that health care was an important aspect of faith. India's priests were also her physicians. The *Rig Veda* outlined these principles, while Lord Brahma, the Hindu creator of the universe and god of all knowledge, emphasized the need for a holistic approach to spiritual and physical wellbeing. This was passed down in the form of Ayurveda, a term made up from two Sanskrit words: *ayu* meaning 'life', and *veda*, meaning 'knowledge'. Hindu mythology tells us about the origins of Ayurveda. Long, long ago mankind was permanently sick. There were so many diseases with little hope of a cure that the sages met on top of the Himalayas to discuss what could be done. They approached Indra, Lord of the Immortals, who had learned about Ayurveda from the twins who acted as doctors to the gods. They, in turn, had learned about it from Brahma.

Ayurveda is a comprehensive and intricate system of medicine that encourages the Indians to deal with the diseased person as a whole, rather than dealing only with disease. Ayurveda sees each person as a unique being made up of five primary *bhutas*, or elements – ether (space), air, fire, water and earth. These elements can combine to create physiological functions that are the Indian equivalent of the four humours found in Greek medicine:

Vata dosha *A combination of earth and air elements. Vata (wind) governs the principle of movement.*

Pitta dosha *A combination of fire and water elements. Pitta (bile) is the process of transformation or metabolism.*

Kapha dosha *A combination of water and earth elements. Kapha (phlegm) is responsible for growth and protection.*

In a healthy body, the *doshas* are in harmony. But when excess *doshas* accumulate, throwing the body out of balance, the immune system is disturbed and illness follows. An Ayurvedic practitioner will suggest supplements, and nutritional and lifestyle changes, to correct the imbalance and restore health.

Rockets

The battle of Pollilur in 1790 has been described as 'one of the greatest calamities that has ever befallen British arms'. Pollilur lies 16 km (10 miles) to the north-west of modern Kanchipuram, India. The battle was fought between the British, commanded by Colonel William Baillie, and the French, who were aided by India's first free-dom fighter, the infamous Tipu Sultan, better known as the Tiger of Mysore. Tipu's artillery included cannon and poison-tipped arrows, but he also had a deadly secret weapon: the rocket. When a rocket managed to ignite one of the British ammunition stores, the battle was all but over. There were further battles in 1792 and 1797 in which Indian rockets were also decisive.

The Chinese had invented the rocket around AD 1000, as an instrument of entertainment and war, and the technology eventually spread westwards. India, with her hilly landscape and dry riverbeds, was a difficult country for artillery, but splendid for rockets; one great advantage of rockets is that they don't need heavy cannons – which are difficult to transport – to launch them. What's more, India had good supplies of saltpetre, a vital ingredient of gunpowder. By 1790 rockets were known in the West, but European rockets were made of wood rather than iron; the iron casing allowed Indian rockets to use greater pressure, which led in turn to increased thrust and range.

The Indian rockets varied in size, but generally took the form of an iron tube about 20 cm (8 inches) long and 3–8 cm (1–3 inches) in diameter. The tube was closed at one end, and strapped to a bamboo shaft about a metre long. Then it was filled with combustible material and gunpowder – a large rocket carrying a pound of powder could travel some 900 metres (more than half a mile), and some rockets travelled up to 2.5 km (12 miles). These lethal weapons were not fired at random. The rocket men in Tipu's army were trained to assess the parabolic curve of the rocket's flight and vary the angle of dispatch, depending upon the diameter of the tube and the distance from the target.

Tipu even created a multiple-rocket launcher capable of firing five to ten rockets at once. He occasionally replaced the bamboo guide shaft with an old sword; when the rocket came down at the end of its flight the whole thing tumbled in the air, and a swarm of whirling swords flashing out of the sky must have been terrifying, to say the least. The British were greatly impressed. At the end of the war, hundreds of Indian rockets and rocket parts were sent back to England, for analysis.

Back in England they were taken to an inventive young man called William Congreve. When he was 13 he had suggested that it might be possible to travel to the moon. He was right; it would prove to be possible, although not in the hot-air balloon that he recommended. Congreve realized what the Indians had known for centuries – that rockets don't push against anything on the ground. This means that, unlike a cannon or a gun, there is no recoil, or kickback, when a rocket is launched; as Congreve said, rockets are ammunition without ordnance. This suggested to him that they might be useful at sea, since the recoil was dangerous in ships.

Congreve set to work and adapted the Indian rocket, moving the pole to the centre to make it more accurate. By 1806 he had developed iron-cased rockets weighing 14 kg (30 lb), with guide sticks 4 metres long. The Napoleonic wars were raging, and on 8 October he had the chance to attack Boulogne. Within half an hour the British had fired 200 rockets at the French ships anchored in the harbour. Unfortunately there was a strong wind. Not a single rocket hit a French ship, but by a lucky fluke they set fire to the town, and caused much destruction, which Congreve claimed as a great victory. A year later, 300 rockets were fired at Copenhagen, destroying much of the city and forcing surrender. And at the battle of Leipzig, in 1813, the Royal Artillery Rocket Brigade terrified 2500 French infantry into surrender. In 1815 the Duke of Wellington reluctantly took rockets to Waterloo, where apparently they were useful only to frighten the French horses.

Rockets also saw action in America on 13 September 1814, and as a result they turn up in the United States national anthem, 'The Star-spangled Banner', which includes the lines:

> *And the rockets' red glare, the bombs bursting in air*
> *Gave proof through the night that our flag was still there…*

Perpetual motion

Perpetual-motion machines – machines that perform useful work without any external energy source – have fascinated inventors for hundreds of years. The enormous appeal of perpetual motion rests in the promise of a limitless source of free power. This has never been achieved, and it never will be. Perpetual motion violates the first two laws of thermodynamics, which tell us that:

> *1. The energy of an isolated system is constant. (In simple language, this means that you can't create or destroy energy.)*

2. The entropy of an isolated system increases in the course of a spontaneous change. (A bit more difficult to understand, this one. Basically it means that energy disperses whenever it can – so a hot pan will cool down when it is taken off the cooker because its thermal energy flows out and is lost in the cooler air. The opposite never happens.)

To put it another way, imagine me setting out for a morning bike ride. I start at the end of the garden, go through the streets, uphill to the green spaces, round past the joggers and dog-walkers, and after, say, 5 or 6 miles I come back to the end of the garden. The exact route does not matter; I must have gone exactly as much uphill as downhill, in order to get back to where I started from. It is the same with any cycle, including the cycle of an engine; there is no net energy change after one complete cycle. That is the first law of thermodynamics; whatever the route, you can't win.

Perpetual motion? Bhaskara described a wheel with tubes of mercury around its circumference. He hoped the sloshing mercury would create a continual imbalance that would sustain rotation.

On the other hand, I cannot freewheel all the way. Most of the time I have to pedal, and up the hills I have to work hard. I can never zoom down each hill fast enough to get up the next without pedalling. This is because there is always some loss of energy to friction – friction in the chain, friction between the tyres and the road, and so on. That is the second law of thermodynamics; you can't even break even.

The knowledge that perpetual motion is an impossible dream has in no way stopped inventors throughout the world from attempting to create perpetual-motion machines. Indeed, people have been 'inventing' perpetual-motion machines for so long now that the US patent office demands a working model, and issues a strict warning that inventors attempt to register their inventions at their own peril – under no circumstances will registration fees be refunded if the machine is found not to work.

So where did the idea of perpetual motion come from? India, of course. In about AD 1150 the great mathematician Bhaskara, drawing on earlier scientific and astronomical work of the great thinker Brahmagupta, designed two wheels that he believed would turn forever. The first wheel had hollow spokes half filled with mercury. The second wheel had a narrow channel in the rim, half filled with mercury and half filled with water. The two wheels would not have turned in perpetuity. That hardly matters. The stimulus provided by this idea sparked a huge amount of thinking about the nature of mechanical power.

Town planning

Most ancient cities, Thebes, Athens and Rome included, evolved without any sort of formal planning. They were untidy, dark, dirty and criss-crossed by narrow, winding streets that made transport difficult. Workshops, slum housing, temples and palaces sat uncomfortably side by side. These early cities were crowded, and this, combined with the lack of sanitation, led inevitably to disease.

The towns built by the Harappans of the Indus Valley in 2300 BC were entirely different, because they were planned from scratch. They had wide, flat main roads that allowed the use of wheeled transport, a sophisticated drainage system, and wells and canals to provide fresh water (see plates, page 8).

Mohenjo-Daro, in the Sind region of Pakistan, is the best known of the Indus Valley cities. Its builders used baked mud bricks, which have survived remarkably well to the present day. Like many other Indus cities, Mohenjo-Daro was built in two sections, a smaller citadel and a large 'lower town'. The walled citadel sat on top of a substantial brick platform. Here were the public and religious buildings that serviced the city, including a granary, an asphalt-lined Great Bath, which was presumably used for ritual cleansing, and a large, colonnaded hall.

The lower town was home to at least 20,000 people, who lived in two-storey houses and barracks. Here the main roads, up to 10 metres wide, were laid out in a regular grid pattern running north, south, east and west. Secondary streets linked the housing to the main roads. The richer houses had bathrooms and lavatories, linked by covered drains to an underground sewerage system. We know of only one place in the world that boasts earlier lavatories – the settlement of Skara Brae on Orkney (see page 13). The lower town also housed the workshops that provided the citizens with pottery, beads, stone and metal tools, and cloth. However, neither the citadel nor the lower town has provided evidence of anything resembling a royal palace.

Zero

The number-one invention of the ancient Indians was nothing. Nought. Zero. It revolutionized mathematics. When it travelled to the West at the end of the twelfth century, nothing was *really* something. And that was not all. Along with zero travelled the numerals 1, 2, 3, 4, 5, 6, 7, 8 and 9. We call them Arabic numerals, and words such as zero are Arabic, because the Arabs brought the numbers to the West, but originally these numerals came from India. I love the fantasy image of a young Indian inventor running into a great hall, shouting with excitement that he had come up with the ultimate invention, and when questioned saying proudly that it was nothing. 'Here! This empty box! Zero is better even than sliced bread.'

Why did nothing matter so much? Before the arrival of the Indian numbering system, with only Roman numerals to work with, we struggled with relatively simple maths.

MMDCCCVIII
(M=1000, D=500, C=100, L=50, X=10,V=5, I=1)

Any literate medieval scholar would have known this represents two thousand eight hundred and eight. Any modern reader (armed with a calculator, perhaps) will be able to divide this number by 4. But try dividing it by IV, on paper, using the Roman numerals.

In the same way, try multiplying VII by XI and then multiplying the result by XIII; do you get MI? Working with such figures is very difficult because there is no system of number placing, or 'hundreds, tens and units', and no symbol for zero. We have to translate the Roman numbers into our own system before we can work with them. As a result of the awful Roman numerals, mathematical computations in the medieval world were the preserve of a specialized, gifted few, who used abacuses (counting frames) rather than parchment or paper. Competent mathematicians were believed to have almost supernatural powers.

But in India mathematicians devised a much better system for arithmetic. In AD 499, the mathematician and astronomer Aryabhata wrote an important text explaining the Indian method for recording and manipulating numbers. Aryabhata used just ten symbols – 1, 2, 3, 4, 5, 6, 7, 8, 9 and 0 – but he allocated his symbols a specific place in each number. The new symbols could be placed in front of a succession of zeros. To the Romans, four was written IV, forty XXXX, four hundred CCCC and four thousand MMMM. Using the Indian system, however, the position of the 4 helped determine the size of the number. With the help of the zero to show empty places to the right, it could become 40, or 400 or 4000.

Not everyone was happy to convert to the new number system. Some traditionalists, the Catholic Church included, denounced the newfangled maths as a heresy and clung with misplaced loyalty to their Roman numerals and abacuses. They could only watch with envy as their more forward-thinking colleagues started doing complicated sums on paper. Eventually, the advantages of the new technique could no longer be denied, for it allowed difficult sums to be done in a matter of minutes.

Curiously, although the Indian number system depends on zero, and makes counting and calculating far simpler, we don't actually use the zero when we count. Look at your fingers; which is number zero? Have you ever seen a house numbered zero? When zero appears in a number we don't mention it; we say 'ten' or 'two hundred and three' or 'five million' without giving the zero any credit at all. Nevertheless, Albert Einstein once remarked 'The Indians taught us how to count.'

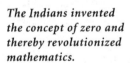

The Indians invented the concept of zero and thereby revolutionized mathematics.

V

THE CHINESE

China was not the first of the great civilizations; Sumer and Egypt were certainly established earlier. But it did (and still does) possess one formidable asset: continuity. China boasts the oldest civilization in history, stretching back in an unbroken line for over four thousand years. This continuity has given the Chinese a wonderful advantage, for they did not lose a host of scientific ideas and technologies each time a civilization collapsed, which happened time and again in the West. They were able to build upon earlier advances, with the result that, between AD 400 and the mid-1600s, the Middle Kingdom (as the Chinese refer to their country) was undoubtedly the most technologically and scientifically advanced society on the planet.

We still owe an immense amount to China's civilization and the ingenuity of its people. Printing, silk, tea, paper money, the iron suspension bridge, fine ceramics, steel, the compass, the drive belt and the chain drive were all invented by the Chinese. Many of their most successful inventions were avidly taken up by the West, sometimes arriving by a slow diffusion of ideas across the Eurasian continent, or, after 1600 and the European Age of Discovery, via the galleons and gunboats of the western powers.

And yet, although the Chinese made so many innovations, often many hundreds of years ahead of the West, they are no longer the world's technological leaders.

War and wheelbarrows

Ironically enough, early Chinese alchemists were mixing a multitude of compounds in their pursuit of the elusive elixir of life, when they stumbled on a deadly mixture. The first mention of what they called *Huo Yao* (fire chemical), is in a ninth-century Daoist book, where there is a strong admonition against the mixing together of sulphur, charcoal and saltpetre (potassium nitrate), and a warning that several alchemists who ignored this injunction had been burnt, or their houses had even been destroyed.

While everyone knows that the Chinese invented gunpowder, we in the West have been too ready to believe that they used it only for amusement and fireworks. Their original formula had a relatively small proportion of nitrate in the mixture, which meant the mix ignited with a 'whoosh' rather than with devastating speed. Despite this the Chinese were soon using the 'fire chemical' in military rocket-arrows, grenades and even an early form of flame-thrower. When they discovered that increasing the amount of nitrate produced a more violent explosion (by providing extra oxygen for the reaction) things took off in a big way. They made bombs that were far more destructive than the earlier weapons, and used them for really big projects, like destroying city walls or breaking down heavy wooden gates.

The fire-lance also appeared around this time. It was really a rocket back-to-front on a stick, with the propulsive end pointing forward. The warrior held the stick and pointed the jet of burning gunpowder towards the enemy. The weapon was good for a three-minute burn, and was excellent for protecting city walls against an assault by ladder-climbing foes.

Bamboo was used to contain the gunpowder of the fire-lance, and the availability of this natural tubing led inevitably to the next advance in firepower. The kick or recoil from the weapon, combined with the new, more explosive gunpowder mix, seems to have given some bright spark the idea of combining the two innovations. Stones and sharp shards of pottery were added to the gunpowder mixture, so that when the weapon was ignited the explosion threw the missiles into the faces of the enemy. The fire-lance had evolved into a primitive cannon. The technology was rapidly improved; an enormous advance was to replace the bamboo barrel with a metal casing. Soon, during the early Yuan dynasty (around 1280), the mass of small missiles was abandoned in favour of a single large 'ball' that almost completely blocked the cannon's muzzle, and allowed the weapon to harness the full propulsive force of the new high-nitrate gunpowder. The cannon proper had arrived.

The first cannons, called bombards, were short, pot-bellied weapons, hopelessly inaccurate, yet immensely effective against large targets like fortifications or massed troops. Cannons, grenades and bombs came into widespread use and were deployed with great effect against barbarian invasions, and in battles between warring dynasties.

When cannons finally reached western Eurasia, probably around 1327, they heralded the end of medieval feudalism. European society was centred around heavily armoured aristocratic knights, whose lands and privileges were guaranteed by their possession of relatively impregnable castles. Both knight and castle, however, were frighteningly vulnerable to cannon and gunpowder – and the effect on Europe was literally shattering.

By contrast, this new destructive technology had little lasting effect on the Middle Kingdom in China; people and property might be destroyed more efficiently, but the society itself, governed by a unique and far less vulnerable feudal bureaucracy, took the development of gunpowder in its stride. You could even say that the material contributed to the survival of the state on many occasions. At the battle of Tshai Shih on the Yangtse River in 1161, the Jurchen Tartars led by their emperor, Wanyen Liang, were comprehensively trounced by the Chinese Sung dynasty's fleet, which made devastating use of gunpowder. The Tartar emperor was assassinated by his own men before the invaders retreated north, leaving the Sung dynasty intact.

But gunpowder was not the only Chinese invention that helped to save the Sung. The Chinese forces were equipped with another cunning piece of Middle Kingdom technology, a weapon so effective it was given its own secret code-names. We call it the wheelbarrow.

The Chinese wheelbarrow is a different beast from the vehicle we know so well from building sites and DIY projects. The western version has its wheel at one end, its handles at the other. The wheel takes around half the weight of the material being carried in the wheelbarrow, leaving the operator to lift the other half and provide all the motive power. There's little doubt that it derived originally from an even more primitive carrying device: the stretcher. In effect, the wheelbarrow is a one-man stretcher, with the wheel standing in for the lead stretcher-bearer, taking part of the weight, but without helping to provide any forward momentum.

Chinese wheelbarrows come in a multitude of sizes and types, but the most characteristic structure is dominated by an enormous wheel placed in the very centre of the carrying bay. At first sight this

Some Chinese wheelbarrows had sails to provide forward power.

looks like madness, but it is in fact a sublimely sensible arrangement. The single wheel is highly manoeuvrable, and makes the barrow eminently suitable for the narrow, twisting tracks that characterized most of China's transport system in times past. And because it is centrally placed all the weight being carried is directed, via the axle, down through the spokes of the wheel to the rim and thence to the ground. In effect, whereas the wheel in a European wheelbarrow replaces the lead stretcher-bearer, in China it replaces a pack animal and carries all the load. So, once the barrow is upright and balanced, the operator has no weight to carry and all he has to do, apart from keeping the wheelbarrow balanced, is push it where he wants it to go. The load is limited by the weight the operator can push, whereas in a European design it is limited by the maximum weight that can be held aloft by the strength of the operator's arms, shoulders and back, plus the effort required to push. As a result, any given load can be carried further with less effort by the eastern version.

The man usually credited with the invention of this most useful machine is Chuko Liang, a famous general of the kingdom of Shu, whose army used it to transport troops and supplies during the many campaigns he undertook in the third century AD. Wheelbarrows could also, if necessary, be set in a circle to defend against cavalry attacks, foreshadowing the Boer's laager by more than a thousand years. When gunpowder appeared on the scene the barrow was converted to a rocket battery, and highly manoeuvrable wheelbarrow rocket-squadrons were able to fire massed salvos at the enemy. So useful did the wheelbarrow prove, it was classified as 'secret' and was given various code-names in several reports:

In the ninth year (Chuko) Liang again came forth from Qi Shan, transporting supplies on 'Wooden Oxen'. ...
In the spring of the twelfth year...knowing that the main army would come out from Yeh-ku, he used 'Gliding Horses' to transport supplies.

The 'wooden ox' was a wheelbarrow with handles in the front, for pulling; the 'gliding horse' had push-handles at the back.

In fact, the wheelbarrow was invented at least a hundred years earlier: scenes depicted on tiles and tomb carvings clearly show the one-wheeled vehicle in a number of situations. It seems that General Chuko Liang gained the credit by being the first to realize the military value of this primitive-looking but effective machine.

However, the Chinese were not content to leave the wheelbarrow simply as a man-powered, one-wheeled pushcart. Pack animals were frequently harnessed to the vehicles, most often mules or donkeys. But perhaps the most spectacular aspect of the story of the Chinese wheelbarrow was the invention of a sail-powered version to carry it effortlessly across the plains. In the early 1790s, the Dutch trader A. E. van Braam could hardly believe his eyes when:

> ...today I saw a whole fleet of wheelbarrows of the same size. I say, with deliberation, a fleet, for each of them had a sail, mounted on a small mast exactly fixed in a socket arranged at the forward end of the barrow. The sail, made of matting, or more often of cloth, is five or six feet high, and three or four feet broad, with stays, sheets and halyards, just as on a Chinese ship. The sheets join the shaft of the wheelbarrows and can thus be manipulated by the man in charge...I could not help admiring the combination, and was filled with sincere pleasure in seeing twenty or so of these sailing-wheelbarrows setting their course one behind the other.

Accounts of this technology reached the West from other sources, becoming garbled in the process and leading to the belief that the Chinese possessed sailed carriages that could transport their owners, and several friends, over vast distances at unheard-of speeds 'driven forwards by the Winde as if they were in the Water...'. In the sixth century there is even a report of a wind-driven carriage that could transport 30 men and travel several hundred *li* in the course of a single day (a *li* is about 600 metres). The specifications for this wondrous machine – if it was not the product of a fertile imagination – appear to have been lost almost as soon as they were created. The idea of the sailing wheelbarrow appealed to the popular imagination, and even found its way into Milton's *Paradise Lost*, where the poet declaims on the barren plains:

> *Of Sericana, where Chineses drive*
> *With Sails and Wind their canie waggons light…*
> (Paradise Lost III)

Such conceits produced a most unexpected result. Inspired by the imagined invention of the Chinese, Europeans began their own experiments in wind-powered carriages. In 1600 a brilliant Dutch scientist and engineer, Simon Stevin, built two wind carriages that were able to travel the 50 or so miles between Scheveningen and Petten in under two hours. Given that their speed cannot have been constant throughout, the carriages must have achieved speeds unheard of in those days, and well in excess of 50 km per hour (30 m.p.h.). Although such experiments proved to be a dead end as far as land travel was concerned, they did have far-reaching consequences as they were the first to accustom the European mind to the possibility of high-speed land travel, a concept that was to flower two hundred years later when steam power was developed.

Fabric, football and food

In classical antiquity the rarest and most expensive clothing, the Armani and Versace of the time, was made of silk. No one in the West was quite sure how the fibres of this wonderfully cool and smooth material were produced; all they knew was that the only supply came from a land far to the east, a land the Romans called Serica (land of silk).

Serica was China, and the source of the fabulous silk-fibre was a Chinese insect: the silk moth (*Bombyx mori*). The larval form hatches from an egg and spends the next 30 days voraciously consuming the leaves of just one plant: the white mulberry. When it is full-size and ready to turn into an adult silk moth, the caterpillar spins itself a protective cocoon composed of a single strand of silk of enormous length, several hundred metres of continuous fibre forming a pupal case. Silk possesses enormous tensile strength – it is at least as strong as steel wire of the same diameter. Safe within this protective shell the process of metamorphosis is completed, and around 15 days later an adult silk moth emerges, ready to feed, mate and continue its life cycle.

As early as the fourteenth century BC, almost 3500 years ago, the people of the Middle Kingdom knew all about the silk moth and had realized just how useful this creature's home could be. The enormous length of a silk fibre and its great strength made the material better than any known plant fibre (this remains true even today). The Chinese devised an ingenious way of unspinning the cocoon and using the fibre to weave their own protective coverings in the form of beautiful cloaks, tunics and gowns (see plates, page 9). They collected the cocoons and soaked them in a hot-water bath. This killed the developing insects, and at the same time loosened the fibres and allowed a continuous silk strand to be reeled off each pupal case.

Such was the demand for this wonderful fibre, the Chinese began the systematic farming of silk moths, which developed into a wonderfully sound ecological cycle. Sheep were kept next to the silkworm houses, and their manure fed the mulberry trees (one animal produced enough manure to fertilize one *mu* (about 800 sq yds) of trees), whose leaves fed the silkworms in summer and the sheep in winter. Completing the cycle, the droppings from the silkworms in turn helped to feed the sheep, for they were used to fertilize rice paddies on which the sheep grazed in due season.

Producing a material as useful as silk in such quantity had an added effect. It stimulated the Chinese to invent various machines to process the fibres more efficiently, including the drive belt and chain drive, and a treadle-powered silk-winding machine with an innovative 'flyer' to lay the silk down evenly on the reel. Thanks to the strange cocoon of *Bombyx mori*, for more than a thousand years Chinese textile machinery was far in advance of anything found in the West.

Silk, in the form of a silk net, was also important in a sport that most westerners consider a wholly British invention: the game of football. Tradition was that the sport derived from the medieval practice of kicking and carrying a leather bag between two goals in opposing villages, an ancient and violent tradition that could go on for days and left many of the participants bleeding and injured. But recent research has shown that a pastime current in early China casts a new, Eastern light on the origins of the Beautiful Game.

The Chinese game, *T'su chu*, originated around the third century BC and was immensely popular – in some dynasties even the emperor enjoyed a kick-around with his friends. It is still played today. The objective was to kick a leather ball through a 'goal' made of a silken net. Just as in modern-day soccer, there was a 'handball' rule – only the feet could be used to move the ball. The parallels with the 'English' game are compelling and it seems that, in the contest for inventor of football, the UK may well have to concede victory to the Chinese team.

What could be better, after a game of *T'su chu*, than a quick snack to replace all that energy. The Middle Kingdom came up with some of the world's earliest fast-food restaurants: the noodle stalls still to be seen on the streets of every Chinese city. The ingredients of noodles are simplicity itself – they are made from flour and water, sometimes with the addition of egg – but the kneading and drawing out of the dough into its correct proportions is a skilled operation that takes years of practice to perfect. Once dried, noodles have a shelf life of months, if not years, yet they can be cooked in less than five minutes to form a filling and highly satisfying staple of the Chinese diet.

If you think this all sounds suspiciously like Italian pasta, you are right on target. But the Chinese definitely got there first – they have been making pasta-based delicacies for well over a thousand years, long before the Italians even thought of the idea. In fact, it is said that Marco Polo brought this culinary innovation back with him to Venice after his adventures in China. There are great similarities between the two cuisines. 'Ants and trees', a recipe from Sichuan province, is a mixture of noodles and minced beef in a pungent sauce (the mince clinging to the noodles looks to the Chinese like ants climbing along the branches of a tree). The dish instantly recalls spaghetti bolognese – spaghetti, after all, is just another name for noodles. And it is true that not only 'spaghetti', but also the precursors of cannelloni, ravioli and many other pasta dishes can be seen at food stalls throughout China. So, as well as the delights of Italian cuisine, we can also blame the Chinese for that modern gastronomic horror, the pot noodle.

What would go well with a bowl of noodles? A nice cup of tea, of course. The British have been drinking tea for over 300 years, but the Chinese may have been drinking it for almost 5000! Legend tells how one day the Emperor Shen Nung sat in the shade of a bush while his servant boiled a pan of drinking water. A dry leaf fluttered down from the bush and landed in the boiling water. Shen Nung, being a keen experimental botanist, decided to try the fragrant brew and found it both tasty and refreshing. A new drink had been discovered. Archaeologists cannot confirm the story of Shen Nung and his floating leaf, but they do know that by the Tang Dynasty (618–906 AD) tea had become the national drink of China.

At least the Chinese have the good sense not to eat their noodles out of a plastic pot – or do they? Many meals in China are eaten from beautifully carved, lacquered wooden bowls; and the protective lacquer coating is actually a natural plastic, a vegetable varnish of remarkable strength and durability. The technique of producing and applying it as a decorative barrier was discovered by the inhabitants of the Middle Kingdom almost four thousand years ago. Lacquer comes from the sap of the Asian lacquer tree (*Verniciflua* spp.)

which is found in mountainous regions over a wide area of the Far East at an altitude of between 1000 and 2500 metres. The sap is obtained by a process analogous to rubber 'tapping': the bark of the tree is scored with a sharp knife and the sap that oozes from the wound is collected in small metal pots. The harvest is tiny, rarely more than 50 g (2 oz), and the tree must be left to recover for between five and seven years. Once collected, the sap is filtered to remove impurities and left to thicken slightly before use.

Fortunately it blends readily with pigments or other additives to produce a wide range of finishes. Three layers of raw lacquer are normally enough to achieve a protective coating, but the Chinese took their innovation much further, creating beautiful works of art that required up to a hundred individual coats of lacquer. Each coat was allowed to dry, then carefully polished before the application of the next one, a painstaking operation that produced bowls and table-ware of unsurpassed quality (see plates, page 9). Sometimes (and especially during the Yuan period, AD 1279–1368) the surface of the lacquer was intricately carved and inlaid with mother-of-pearl, silver or gold. The technique spread to Japan as early as the eighth century AD, and was enthusiastically taken up by its craftsmen, but lacquerwork remained unknown in the West until the time of the Renaissance. Like the Japanese, westerners immediately realized the value of the new product, and a brisk trade developed. European artisans even tried to emulate the technique using a gesso base covered with varnish (so-called japanning), but the imitation lacquerwork fell far short of the original, both in beauty and in strength.

Once applied, lacquer confers astonishing protection to the wood it covers. It is waterproof, resistant to termites and bacterial attack, and impervious to both strong acids and alkalis. Perhaps even more remarkable, lacquered wood will not burn in a normal flame; it is unaffected by temperatures below 400°C. This means you can actually use a lacquered wooden bowl to boil water over an open fire and it will not burn.

Furnaces and flame-throwers

Every fire needs oxygen, and the more it can get the harder and the hotter it will burn. Stone Age people surely knew this, and blew air into dying campfires to rekindle the blaze in order to cook food or keep themselves warm. When metalworking was invented, keeping a constant flow of air to achieve and maintain a high temperature became a more serious problem.

Gold can be found (in the right places) in the form of the shiny yellow metal itself, but most other metals come in the form of ores, their oxides or salts. Iron, for example, occurs naturally in various salts and also as oxides, especially haematite. This is a red rock, the same colour as rust (which is iron oxide), and the same colour as the planet Mars, whose surface is covered in iron-rich minerals.

To make iron metal, metalworkers have to reduce the oxide to the metal by taking away the oxygen. The best way to remove it is with carbon, and by trial and error it was found that a good form of this is charcoal. So they heated iron ore with charcoal; a process called 'smelting'. The carbon reacts with the oxygen to make carbon dioxide, which comes off as a gas leaving iron behind.

This is the basic process. However, you need a high temperature both to make sure the reaction is complete and also to melt the iron, which will otherwise be mixed with all sorts of impurities – leftover ore, charcoal, other minerals, camel dung and so on. Iron melts at about 1500°C – bright yellow heat – and early metallurgists were unable to achieve this temperature. However, in furnaces at, say, 1100°C they could reduce the iron oxide and make 'blooms' – spongy lumps of red-hot iron that could be hammered into shape. This wrought iron was impure, but nevertheless strong and useful.

Copper is much easier to extract and work, because it melts at a lower temperature than iron – 1083°C – which is why the Bronze Age (bronze is an alloy of tin and copper) came before the Iron Age.

Getting and maintaining high furnace temperatures was important for all metalworkers, and in both East and West they raised

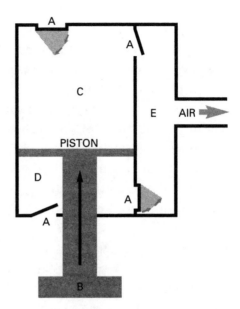

The double-action piston-bellows uses flap-valves (A) to control the flow of air. When the handle B is pushed up, air is drawn into the large box D through the hole in the bottom, and pushed out into box E through the valve near the top. When B is pulled down, air is pulled into C through the hole in the top and out into E through the valve near the bottom. Thus the bellows deliver an almost continuous stream of air through the tube on the right.

them by using bellows, either simple inflated skins or more advanced 'squeeze-box' types. However, these were extremely tiring to use, and needed to be worked in pairs to produce a constant supply of air. They were inefficient, labour-intensive and unreliable.

The Chinese were the first to overcome these disadvantages and they did so, with their customary simplicity and ingenuity, with the double-action piston-bellows, which they invented in the fourth century BC. Easily constructed from wood, this rectangular 'box bellows' is really two boxes in one. The larger compartment is the intake cylinder. Inside it is a piston, the edges of which are lined with either soft paper or feathers, to make a relatively airtight fit with the walls. At each end of the compartment is a simple flap- or clack-valve, a hinged 'door', that allows air into the chamber when the piston is being pulled away from the valve, but slams shut when the piston reverses direction. So each time the piston handle is pushed or pulled, air is drawn into the box. At the same time, air is pushed out of this larger box into the smaller one through another valve, and from there a near-continuous stream of air is blown to fan the fire.

The push-pull action of the Chinese piston-bellows means it was far less tiring to use than western bellows of the period, and with the new invention only one man was required to ensure a continuous stream of air for the furnace. With such 'perpetual bellows' the Chinese were able to reach and maintain far higher temperatures, allowing the smelting of both copper and iron. Amazingly, they were producing cast-iron utensils and other implements as early as the fifth century BC, while in the West comparable artefacts do not appear until almost a thousand years later.

The Chinese soon came to realise that their invention was useful not only for gases – it could also drive a continuous stream of liquid. From the early eleventh century (i.e., before the battle of Hastings, when western Europeans were still fighting with bows and arrows), they put the system to work in a terrifying military application: the flame-thrower. It was known as the *fang meng huo yu* (fierce fire oil shooter) and was particularly useful in defending cities against a mass attack, or for clearing city walls of attackers. The weapon consisted of a 'lance', essentially a long, brass cylinder, connected by pipes to a reservoir of fuel – usually naphtha, a mixture of liquid hydrocarbons rather like petrol. At the front of the lance was a spear-shaped 'firebox' containing slow-burning material such as a wick or 'match' that behaved like a pilot light, while at the other end a push-pull handle allowed the operator to move the internal piston to and fro. Using a double-piston version of the air pump, fuel was forced under pressure from the reservoir through a small nozzle at the front of the lance and ignited by the firebox, then sprayed out in a constant jet of flame towards the enemy.

In the West the Byzantine empire possessed a flame-thrower of sorts at around the same time. It was known as the 'siphon', and used the same flammable ammunition as its oriental counterpart (naphtha was known locally as 'Greek fire'), but it could do no more than shoot brief, intermittent bursts of flame at the foe – in contrast to the Chinese weapon which, by using the double-action piston-bellows, spouted a continuous stream of fire at the enemy. The device was apparently easy to use, and there are accounts of mandarins being disparaged because their skill with the 'fierce fire oil shooter' surpassed their mastery of calligraphy, an essential art in ancient China. Nevertheless, the weapon gave good service in many wars and insurrections, especially against the Chin Tartars and, later, the Mongol hordes who attacked the country from the north.

Musical measurements

One of the oldest uses for the double-action piston-bellows was in melting bronze to cast bells. The bell is a fairly ubiquitous object in both East and West, though it is believed that, once again, the Chinese had the idea first. Archaeological researchers have discovered a sort of stone xylophone in ancient tombs in China, made of a series of suspended rocks that sound out a scale when struck with a hammer, and this may have given the Chinese the idea of making something similar out of metal. But they took the concept much further, and used certain bells as the basis of a measuring system that encompassed the whole empire.

The system was based on a simple scientific fact. If a bell of a certain pitch is sounded, it is possible to reproduce that same pitch on a stringed instrument by varying the length and tension of the string until the desired note is reached. If the string is composed of a standard material and thickness, then another string, of the same length and tension, will produce the same note anywhere in the world.

The Chinese took this information and used it to standardize the measurement of volume. They used an instrument called a *chun* (similar to a Japanese one-stringed fiddle but, at 2 metres long, much larger) to reproduce the note of a specially chosen bell whose internal volume was the standard 'grain scoop' size. Once they had defined the length and tension of the *chun*'s string, this information could be sent to every province. As the note required on the *chun* was known, bells that produced this same note could be cast, and would then act as templates for all the grain scoops in each of the provinces. An imperial decree gives just such instructions: 'The Chung vessel or bell is to be standard and the magnitude of the pitch should not exceed that produced also by the string of the *chun*, and its weight should not exceed 120 *catties*.'

The decree required that bell-founders be expert in casting bells that produced definite pitches – but this, too, was one of the many skills in which the Middle Kingdom was far in advance of the West. The Chinese went on to base length, volume and weight measurements on the pitch of bells, a standardization that was not seen in Europe until hundreds of years later.

The seismograph

Earthquakes occur when the large plates that make up the earth's surface do not slide easily against one another, but become stuck. Pressure builds, and is finally resolved in a catastrophic release – the plates spring past each other and the energy stored in the plates radiates out in the form of elastic waves. When one of these passes any given point it makes the earth quake, moving rapidly up and down, or from side to side, often with disastrous consequences.

China is situated in one of the most seismically active regions in the world, and catastrophic earthquakes have been common throughout its history. In 1556, an earthquake centred on Shensi province devastated 98 counties and eight provinces of central China, sending out a 480-km (300-mile) wave of destruction from its epicentre. In some areas 6 out of every 10 people were killed, with the final death toll estimated at 830,000, making it the worst natural disaster in the recorded history of the human race. Since 1900, 53 per cent of the total earthquake casualties around the world (over 550,000 people) have been in Chinese territory. Small wonder, then, that the first effective seismograph was constructed in

China in AD 132, over a thousand years before the appearance of de la Hautefeuille's 1703 instrument in the West.

The inventor of this ingenious device was an astronomer, geographer and mathematician called Chang Heng, and a detailed description of his 'earthquake weathercock' was given some time later in the *Hou Han Shu*, the official history of the eastern Han dynasty written in the fifth century AD:

> *It consisted of a vessel of fine cast bronze, resembling a wine jar, and having a diameter of 8* chhih *[2 metres].*

> *It had a domed cover, and the outer surface was ornamented with antique seal-characters and designs of mountains, tortoises, birds and animals.*

Chang Heng's seismograph. In an earthquake the bronze balls were released from the dragons' mouths into the mouths of the toads below.

Inside there was a central column capable of lateral displacement along tracks in the eight directions, and so arranged [that it worked] a closing and opening mechanism.

Outside the vessel there were eight dragon heads, each one holding a bronze ball in its mouth, while round the base sat eight toads with their mouths open, ready to receive any balls which the dragons might drop.

The toothed machinery and ingenious constructions were all hidden inside the vessel, which was topped off with a tightly fitting cover.

When an earthquake occurred, the dragon mechanism of the vessel was caused to vibrate so that a ball was vomited out of a dragon mouth and caught by the toad underneath. At the same instant a sharp sound was made which called the attention of the observers.

Over several years the mechanism proved its worth, as the ball invariably fell into the mouth of the dragon pointing in the direction of the earthquake's epicentre. In fact, the 'earthquake weathercock' exceeded all expectations, as the *Hou Han Shu* explained:

On one occasion one of the dragons let fall a ball from its mouth though no perceptible shock could be felt. All the scholars at the capital were astonished at this strange effect occurring without any evidence [of seismic activity]. But several days later a messenger arrived bringing news of an earthquake... Thenceforward it became the duty of the officials of the Bureau of Astronomy and Calendar to record the directions from which the earthquakes came.

Several attempts have since been made to reconstruct this instrument. All of them assume that the 'central column capable of lateral displacement' refers to an internal pendulum mechanism, though there is some disagreement as to whether this was suspended or inverted (i.e., hinged at the top or bottom). Whatever the true nature of this mechanism, the instrument undoubtedly worked and was considered a triumph by Chang Heng's contemporaries. This is understandable. China's mandarins spent much of their time averting, or coping with, the innumerable problems and disasters of the vast empire – flood, famine, insurrection and earthquake. A device that was capable of giving them early warning that an earthquake had occurred in a far-off district would allow bureaucrats to make their preparations for coping with the inevitable disruption such a catastrophe brought in its wake. That such a sensitive instrument could have been produced from relatively simple technology is a testament to the ingenuity of Chinese scholars and society at the beginning of the Christian era.

Learning to fly

Kite-flying in the West goes back only four hundred years, to around the end of the sixteenth century when the sport was brought back from China by travellers. The kite's Chinese origin is actually implicit in its name – we use the word kite to describe two widely disparate objects: a tethered wind-flying 'sail' and a bird, *Milvus lineatus*. The inhabitants of the Middle Kingdom also used a single word – *yuan* – to designate the same two objects.

The technology behind kite-flying had been known in China since before the birth of Christ. The book *Han Fei Tzu*, written in about 255 BC, recounts that the famous philosopher Mo Tzu 'made a wooden kite that took three years to complete. It could indeed fly, but after one day's trial it was wrecked'. This setback did not deter the Chinese and throughout the first millennium the technology progressed until it eventually became an indispensable adjunct of warfare, with military commanders flying kites that carried hideously painted faces, as well as pipes and strings that gave out unearthly sounds, in order to frighten the opposing forces. At the siege of Khaifeng in 1232, kites were used in the first recorded 'leaflet drop' in history. Many soldiers of the Chin Tartars had been captured by the besieging Mongols, and the defending Chin wanted some way of encouraging the captives to return to their own side. In the *Chin Shih* (a history written around the first or second century AD) we are told: 'The besieged sent up paper kites with writing on them, and when these came over the [enemy] lines, the strings were cut so that they fell among the Chin prisoners. [The messages] incited them to revolt and escape.'

But the Chinese did not stop there. From quite early times they reasoned that if small kites could carry flutes and pipes into the air, larger ones might lift people. There are apocryphal tales from as early as 200 BC of archers carried aloft by giant kites to rain arrows down on the enemy, but by AD 550 there are solid accounts of rather brutal experiments in manned kite flights carried out by the emperor Kao Yang. This bloodthirsty tyrant had recently overcome the powerful Thopa and Yuan families to succeed to the Dragon Throne. When he became a Buddhist he was required to symbolize his conversion by setting free a certain number of birds. Instead, he ordered the surviving Thopas and Yuans to be taken to a particularly high building, the Tower of the Golden Phoenix. Some were fitted out with bamboo-mat 'wings' and cast from the top of the tower. According to the *Chin Shih*, 'this was called a liberation of living creatures. All the prisoners died, but the Emperor contemplated the spectacle with enjoyment and much laughter.'

However, there was more to this than a bizarre execution of rivals. The remaining captives were attached to kites cut out in the form of owls, and launched from the tower to see who could be carried the furthest. This experiment proved more successful. One prisoner, Yuan Huang-Thou, 'was the only one who succeeded in flying as far as the Purple Way (a distance of some 2.5 km/1½ miles), and there he came to earth. But then he was handed over to the

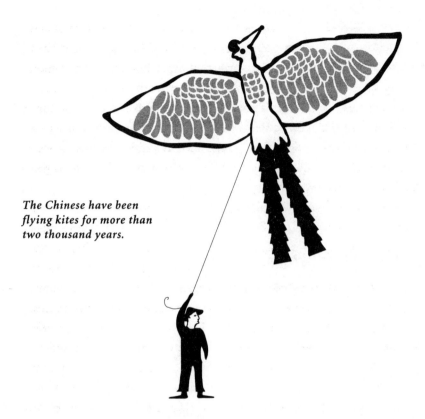

The Chinese have been flying kites for more than two thousand years.

President of the Censorate, who had him starved to death.' Kao Yang was not a kind man.

Kites, like sail-powered wheelbarrows, were impressive, but not impressive enough for the Chinese. Incredibly, over 1600 years ago they were producing flying machines. In an astonishing passage in the *Pao Phu Tzu*, dated to around AD 320, the famous alchemist Ko Hung states that: 'Some have made flying cars with wood, using ox-leather straps fastened to returning blades to set the machine in motion.'

He is clearly describing rotating blades attached to a spinning axle and driven by a (leather) belt – in other words a rotor top, whose principles underlie the modern-day helicopter. And as the description makes clear this was not merely theory that was being discussed – the system worked because flying cars had been made.

The machine, known as the 'bamboo dragonfly', is still used today as a child's toy; it consists of three or four rotor blades (usually made of thin wood or feathers) mounted horizontally, and fixed at an angle to a vertical shaft. A strap or string is wound round the shaft, and when this is pulled sharply it spins the shaft rapidly so that the rotor blades lift the whole mechanism skywards – just like a helicopter. It is tempting to think that the propellers used to drive ships and aeroplanes developed from this same source. In all three systems, the main component the Chinese invention lacked was an efficient motor of sufficient power.

Ships and sailing

If the Chinese lacked the power source to produce a marine engine, they lacked very little else when it came to other naval technology. Even in the thirteenth century their navy numbered some 52,000 men, divided into 20 squadrons. Between about 700 AD and the

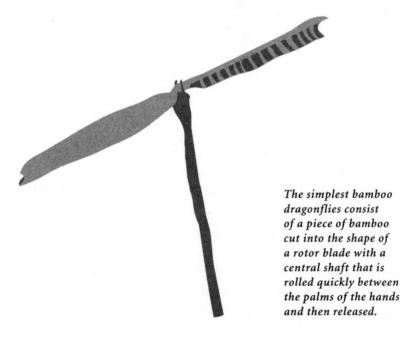

The simplest bamboo dragonflies consist of a piece of bamboo cut into the shape of a rotor blade with a central shaft that is rolled quickly between the palms of the hands and then released.

great era of European exploration the sailors of the Middle Kingdom sailed further than their opposite numbers in the West.

The reason for this is in the very beginning of boat-building, in both areas. In the West boats seem to have been developed from simple dug-out canoes by fitting 'walls' of wood along each side which joined at each end in a sharp, wave-cutting, prow and stern. By contrast, the Chinese design appears to have originated in a raft-like craft, and resulted in the altogether different shape of a typical 'junk' – flat-bottomed and with a box-like stern (see plates, page 9). This difference was to have far-reaching consequences.

Before the birth of Christ, steering oars were used to manoeuvre ships in both China and the West. No one was very satisfied with these, and Europeans experimented with many different arrangements, such as double steering oars attached to a beam. The problem was that oars were vulnerable to damage when two ships came close to each other or when the craft was docking (the Romans even developed a streamlined 'shield' to protect them). The Chinese came up with a central steering oar fitted at the rear of the craft – the parent of the now almost-universal rudder. Their box-stern junks made fitting such an innovation a simple process, whereas even if Europeans had considered the idea, the shape of their ships at that time meant there wasn't really anywhere a rear-end rudder could be fitted. The Chinese rudder was better protected than the Western steering oar, and also allowed the craft to manoeuvre more easily. But the Chinese went one stage further: they purposely cut holes in their rudders, which reduced drag in cross-currents while still retaining the enhanced manoeuvrability of the rear-mounted design.

Chinese boats had highly efficient rigging. The sails were made of bamboo matting and were hung between an upper supporting crosspiece (the yard) and another crosspiece at the bottom (the boom). Many European ships sported a similar design (though the sails were normally made of canvas), but the Chinese added a further innovation and used battens of bamboo to stiffen the whole structure.

These ran across and parallel to the yard and boom, and were laced to the fabric of each sail to keep it very flat, which in turn increased the surface area exposed to the wind.

There were several other advantages to this system. Sheets (ropes) permitted sails to be raised, lowered and furled from the deck, in contrast to the western system of sending sailors aloft to reef them in – a dangerous business, especially in stormy seas. On the rare occasions that men needed to go into the rigging, the battens acted as 'ratlines', making climbing easier and safer. In addition, they allowed for step-wise reefing, with the sails folding in a regular pattern, so the sail area could easily be fine-tuned to prevailing weather conditions. Sails could also be furled quickly, as they fell in pleats when they were lowered. And the system prevented them from being torn and carried away in a full-blown tempest – the battens held them together so that even if a sail, or parts of a sail, were damaged what remained could provide the craft with motive power. Using such ships Chinese sailors explored far and wide. For four years from 1421 fleets of Chinese ships crossed the Pacific and made contact with American Indians on the west coast of America. They explored all of Southeast Asia and Northern Australia, and sailed as far as the coast of East Africa and even Greenland.

Ocean exploring required more than well-designed and sturdy ships – sailors had to know the direction they were travelling in and, just as important, how to get back to China. The machine that was invented to fulfill this requirement is still used today by sailors the world over: the compass.

The compass began life as a tool for feng shui and divining. The Chinese knew about the magnetic properties of lodestone at least two thousand years ago, and used a 'south-pointing spoon' as one of their many fortune-telling techniques. The spoon was a piece of lodestone carved in the shape of the Ursa Major constellation (the Plough, Great Bear or Dipper). It was placed on a square board made of wood or bronze and, balancing on a single point, was pulled by the earth's magnetic field so that the handle pointed to the south. The choice of constellation was significant – in the night sky, the handle of the Plough circles the Pole Star, or North Star, just as the south-pointing handle of the spoon circles the diviner's board. The Chinese geomancer was bringing the heavens down to earth with his equipment; and in so doing he was prefiguring all modern-day pointer-dials and meters.

But the delicate design of the 'south-pointing spoon' made the device useless in rough seagoing conditions, and it was to be several centuries before the next advance: the realization that a thin metal sheet or needle could be magnetized from a lodestone source. When such small and lightweight pointers became available, sailors could determine north and south by floating a needle (or in some cases, a metal 'fish' or 'tadpole') on water, either using surface tension or by attaching the pointer to a sliver of bamboo. Another method, favoured by the astrologer and engineer Shen Gua in AD 1088, was to suspend a magnetized needle 'by a single cocoon fibre of new silk attached to the centre of the needle by a piece of wax the size of a mustard seed – then, hanging in a windless place, it will always point to the south. Among such needles there are some which, after being rubbed, point to the north. I have needles of both kinds by me.'

Chinese compasses consisted of a spoon made of magnetic lodestone placed in the middle of a square board of wood or bronze. The earth's magnetic field causes the spoon's handle to point south.

This was written almost a century before the first compass appeared in Europe, where one of the earliest names for the magnetic needle was *calamita* (tadpole). That this is identical to one of the Chinese names for the same object lends support to the idea that westerners derived the design from a Chinese original.

The Chinese were not only ocean explorers – they were also great inland sailors. Early in their history they possessed an elaborate canal system. In the seventh century AD the emperor decreed that many of the existing canals should be connected and new canals dug to transport rice and other foodstuffs from the south to the northern capital. The Grand Canal, which connected Beijing with the southern towns of the eastern plains, was a monumental building project, equivalent to constructing an artificial river between London and Athens. Because there were many waterways to cross and many ships plying their trade along them, bridges were needed – bridges high enough to allow the passage of sizeable boats. Normal straight ones were out of the question and, because of the formidable width of rivers in China, conventional arched bridges (based on a semicircle) would have been impossibly high. Fortunately, a Chinese engineer soon came up with the answer.

His stroke of genius was to realize that an arch could be effective even if only a small segment of a semicircle was used. The arch would then be very long in comparison to its height, allowing the bridge to span wide rivers with ease. Another plus was that the structure would take less material, and therefore less time, to build. 'Segmental arch bridges' were found all over China long before the design appeared in the West.

The Chinese didn't only build arched bridges – they had suspension bridges too. A suspension bridge is a bridge suspended from cables or chains that pass over pylons or towers and are firmly anchored to the ground (see page 206). The earliest Chinese suspension bridges were made from bamboo rope, bamboo fibres being well suited to bridge building as they have a high tensile strength.

Later the bamboo ropes were replaced with iron chains. The chains needed less maintenance than the ropes, and allowed the engineers to span wider gaps.

Printing and paper money

One way in which the people of the Middle Kingdom transmitted ideas about bridge-building and other inventions was through writing and books. Chinese writing is very different from its western counterpart. It is an ideographic script, where each ideogram represents a word and the characters are written down the page, reading right to left. Despite these differences, the essential idea (of translating spoken language to written form) remains the same, and scrolls and manuscripts were common to both cultures. But whereas westerners seemed content to accept the slow production of texts by hand (hence the word manuscript), in the second century AD the Chinese came up with a far more efficient system: the mass-production of documents by block-printing.

Seal rings and stamps were known in the ancient Middle East, but these 'printed' no more than the owner's name or personal symbol. The Chinese were the first to think of extending this idea so that complete books could be printed en masse, each page cut in relief from a single wood block. In the tenth century AD an anonymous printer attempted to move the technology forward, and suggested printing with movable type, with each character arranged separately and in sequence. This concept (which worked so well when such printing made its journey to the West in the fifteenth century) proved impossible for a language that required upwards of 2000 separate ideograms, and was swiftly abandoned.

The rapid development of printing was chiefly due to two factors. One was religious: the introduction of Buddhism into China early in the sixth century AD. As the new religion prospered many thousands of prayers and sacred texts were required for its eager adherents. Printing was a response to this huge devotional demand. But it could never have got under way without an even earlier Chinese development, and the second factor: the invention of paper.

Legend has it that paper was invented in AD 105 by Cai Lun, an imperial eunuch, and minister of agriculture to the Eastern Han emperor, He Di. However, recent research has pushed the date for papermaking back at least two centuries. The true originator's identity remains unknown. He (or she) is believed to have produced the new, thin, flexible material from pulped wood, rags or netting. The soggy mass of fibres that resulted was laid on a bamboo frame, spread quite thinly and left to dry. Once all the moisture was driven off the newly formed paper was cut into suitable shapes and was ready for use. The Chinese kept the art secret for more than five hundred years, but it was eventually introduced in Japan in 610. The West discovered paper via the Arabs of Moorish Spain, who had learnt the art from Chinese prisoners captured at Samarkand in 768. At this time all paper was handmade on frames. It was not until 1799 that Louis Robert introduced a machine for the continuous production of paper in large rolls.

In China, paper wasn't used only for books. The Chinese made umbrellas, flags and household furnishings out of this useful material; they made toilet paper and even armour, so tough it could resist the strongest arrows. And they came up with an invention that was to have far-reaching consequences and would eventually change the face of the world. This was the first promissory note; in effect, the first paper money. Allegedly, it all began when brigands became so numerous on China's roads that the country's merchants were unable to pay their taxes to the state. Some unknown genius in the mandarinate had the idea of providing them with notes marked with a certain value, which could be exchanged for a set value in gold at the end of their journey. Promissory notes were, in a way, also the first cheques. The idea proved popular with the merchants (who were no longer robbed) and the bureaucrats (who received their taxes) and paper money took off. Today the whole world uses the stuff.

VI

THE GREEKS

The ancient Greek civilization flourished for about a thousand years, not as a unified country but rather as a loose association of city states, both in mainland Greece and elsewhere around the Mediterranean. The philosopher Plato described the states as being like frogs sitting round a pond. Although the Greeks drew on the ideas of various earlier civilizations, they were the people who, more than any others, handed down to us the foundations of our democracy, our notions of ethics and justice, our science, our mathematics and our music. We have a great deal to thank them for.

Health and fitness

Throughout the ancient Greek world there seemed to be a cult of fitness, although this was less about the body beautiful and more about staying alive – men of any age could be called to fight in one of the many wars that cropped up, and basically soldiers were soon divided into the fit and the dead. However, the Greeks also enjoyed sporting contests, and the first Olympic Games were held in 776 BC – an event in which all honourable Greek men were allowed to take part. The long-distance marathon was invented much later to commemorate the heroic achievement of Pheidippides, who in 490 BC ran from Marathon to Athens either to warn of the approaching Persians or to carry the news of their defeat.

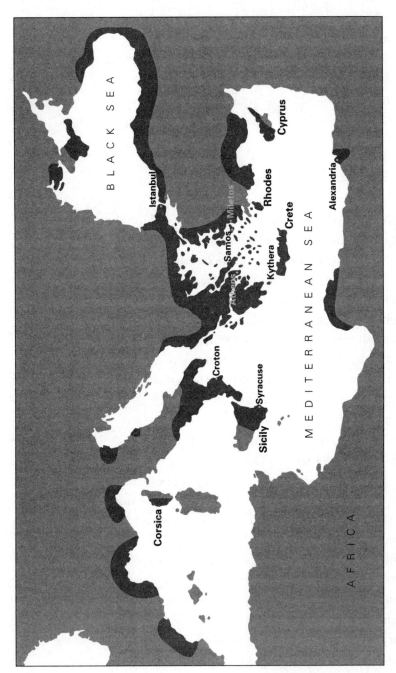

Greater Greece. By 600 BC the Greeks had established colonies around the northern and eastern coasts of the Mediterranean, north Africa and the Black Sea – like frogs sitting around a pond, as Plato described them. In the fourth century BC Alexander the Great pushed the boundaries of the Greek empire further east, across Persia to India.

With all this running and fighting, injuries and death were common, and the wives of Spartans were rumoured to tell their departing husbands to come back with their shields or on them. The lucky ones only broke limbs, and physicians had a clever way of mending broken bones. Suppose you had broken your lower leg. Leather cuffs would be fixed round your knee and your ankle, and the four wooden rods would be jammed between leather cups sewn on the outside of the cuffs, to hold the leg straight against the pull of the muscles and allow the bones to knit. Today you get a plaster cast, but then you got four rods of strong but springy wood. In some ways this was better than a modern plaster cast. Not only did it keep the limb in traction, it also meant that wounds could be treated, and dead skin did not collect inside and cause intense itching.

The Hippocratic bench was a traction device that stretched the whole body to reduce femur fractures, and treat dislocations or back problems. It was named after Hippocrates, the father of Greek medicine, who lived on the island of Kos. He was so well respected as a doctor that a series of books containing a vast collection of medical writings was attributed to him, even though some of the books were written long after he died. His name is also associated with the Hippocratic oath, a vow taken by most doctors in a modern form today; they have to promise to be honest and discreet, and to work for the good of their patients.

Democracy and philosophy in Athens

Democracy means people power, from the Greek *demos* meaning people and *kratos* meaning rule (plutocracy = rule by the rich; autocracy = independent or self-rule). The first movement towards democracy came in Athens soon after 600 BC, and in the next few hundred years the idea spread to many of the Greek city states. Intricate systems were developed for argument and for voting, and there was even a machine – the *kleroterion* – that picked juries.

The smallest jury had 201 people, and in large trials there could be many thousands of jurors. Clearly it was important to make sure they did not all come from the same tribe, or the same place, and the *kleroterion* was a random sampling device. Each juror (adult men only) inserted his identity tag, and balls were then dropped into the side of the machine. Men in the rows with white balls beside their tags were in; those with black balls were out for that day's service.

Practical philosophers

For me, the Greek heroes were the thinkers, some of whom we would call philosophers, starting perhaps with Thales. He lived in Miletos, a city then in Asia Minor (now Turkey), which has been called the cradle of Greek science, and he was a great thinker. One year he made a pile of cash by speculating in olive oil. The story goes that he was taunted by an enemy: 'If you know so much, why aren't you rich?' Thales replied that he wasn't interested in money but, just to show that knowledge could be used for practical purposes, he predicted during the winter that the following olive crop would be spectacular, and leased all the olive presses. When harvest time came he rented them out at high rates, and made a fortune.

I am more interested in the legend that he actually stopped a war in 585 BC by predicting an eclipse of the sun on 28 May. He is said to have warned the generals on both sides that if they did not stop fighting the gods would be seriously annoyed. They ignored him and the sun went out – which scared them enough to stop the war.

Sadly the story is probably untrue. Astronomers don't think Thales could have had enough information to make such a prediction, but the legend illustrates the power of people who knew about the stars. Among other great astronomers was Aristarkhos of Samos, who worked out in about 260 BC that the sun was 20 times bigger than the moon. Even though the real factor is more like 350, what is important is that he was the first person to try to make such measurements. What's more, his method was perfectly valid; the only problem was that his measurements weren't accurate enough.

Aristarkhos made two other shattering assertions. First, he said the fixed stars are immensely distant – much, much further away than the sun, moon and planets – which meant the universe must be millions of times bigger than anyone had thought. Second, and even more radically, he said that the earth goes round the sun, rather than the sun going round the earth. This was a stunning claim, and highly counter-intuitive. Enjoy the sunrise and the sunset, and it seems obvious that you are stationary and the sun is moving. Watch the moon sliding across the sky; or sit in the dark of night and gaze at the endless and beautiful procession of stars rising from the eastern horizon and parading overhead. The earth is 'obviously' still, and all the heavenly bodies go round it. It feels like the centre of the universe.

Aristarkhos, however, reasoned that since the sun is much bigger than the earth, it is unlikely to be revolving round it. What is more, since the stars are enormously far away, they would have to travel immense distances and at fantastic speeds to circle the earth every day. How much simpler if the sun and stars are all still, and their apparent movement is caused by the fact that the earth spins on its axis.

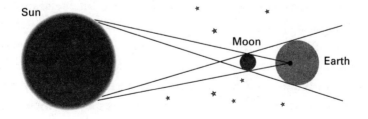

Eclipse of the sun. When the moon passes between the sun and the earth, its shadow races across the landscape, and for a few minutes day becomes night.

Four hundred years later Ptolemy, or Claudius Ptolemaeus, decided he was wrong – if the earth was spinning as fast as Aristarkhos's theory suggested, a stone thrown into the air would get left behind – and in the *Almagest* he was so convincing about the earth being the centre of the universe that everyone believed him until Copernicus came along 1400 years later. Nevertheless Aristarkhos was right. The earth is not the centre of the universe; it spins on its axis and orbits around the sun, as do the other planets in our solar system.

The first computer?

Knowing how the sun, moon and planets moved was so important to the Greeks that they were not content with a book that described these movements. Some unknown genius actually built a machine to predict them far into the future.

Mountainous, barren Crete is by far the largest of the Greek islands, and looks almost like a barrier between Egypt and the rest of Greece. Sail north-west from there and you get to the island of Kythera. Just before you reach it, however, there is another tiny island which, with geographical logic, is called Antikythera, from the Greek prefix *anti-* or *ante-* meaning before (as in anticipate and antenatal).

In 1900 some sponge divers who had been driven off course in a gale discovered a shipwreck 40 metres down on the seabed at Antikythera, and recovered bronze statues and other artefacts. These suggested that the ship had sunk in about 70 BC, sailing from Rhodes to Kos, and had perhaps been on its way to Rome. Among all this booty was a curious lump of bronze some 30 cm (12 in) high. It was corroded and covered with barnacles, but seemed to be a box containing some sort of mechanism (see plates, page 10).

The Antikythera Mechanism lay for decades in the National Archaeological Museum in Athens and defied the efforts of many scientists to unravel its secrets, partly because it was coated in a calcified layer that could be removed only very slowly by skilled technicians. The outside of the box turned out to carry complex astronomical inscriptions, apparently written soon after 100 BC.

In the 1950s an American archaeologist, Derek da Solla Price, became fascinated by the mechanism and determined to find out what it was. Unable to see much from the outside, he guessed that X-rays might help and took it to a hospital where he persuaded the X-ray department to take photographs. He discovered that the mechanism looked rather like an eighteenth-century clock, with three dials on the outside and a complex train of 32 cogwheels inside. All the metal parts had been cut from a single sheet of bronze, about 2 mm (⅛ in) thick.

His investigations took many years but gradually, as the various layers of cogwheels were revealed, he worked out that the mechanism must have been a mechanical calculator or analogue computer, designed to predict the movements of the sun, the moon and the planets. More recently, Michael Wright has reconstructed the mechanism by cutting his own bronze gears, and has included what he believes must be missing parts that would have been needed to predict the movements of all the planets known at the time.

The Antikythera mechanism is unique. Archimedes had a mechanical model of the solar system, but it was was not described in detail and did not survive. Hero of Alexandria and the Roman writer Vitruvius describe various gears and how they are used, but these are hardly more complex than three cogs at a time. No other examples of intricate geared machines from the first century BC have been found. The Greeks were remarkably skilled mechanics as well as philosophers.

Like most astronomical instruments in Greece, the Antikythera mechanism was based on mathematics, which was where the Greeks really shone. In particular, geometry was crucial to one of my favourite Greek inventions: the tunnel through a mountain on the very island where Aristarkhos had lived.

The Samos tunnel

The island of Samos is about as far east as you can get in Greece; within swimming distance is Turkey, the coastal fringe of which was then called Ionia. The main city was also called Samos, and in 500 BC had a population of some 20,000. It lay on the south side of the island, where today is the modest town renamed Pythagorion. Ever since the time of Kolaios, who in about 640 BC 'discovered' the silver mines of Spain, the Samians had been rich, and in the following century they got richer on passing trade. Samos was at one of the crossroads of the ancient world, and the perfect place for plunder and piracy, ably carried out by the ruthless tyrant Polycrates. Not surprisingly, the Samians had built their city walls high. But there was a problem. The city's only constant supply of fresh water came from a spring, now called Agiade, which bubbles up out of the ground on the other side of Mount Kastro.

The engineer Eupalinos of Megara reckoned they should tunnel through the mountain to ensure a secure water supply. He calculated the best place and direction – on the north side of the mountain, slightly downhill from the spring – and in about 550 BC the Samians started digging.

This was an immense project. The mountain is 240 metres high and a kilometre (about half a mile) wide, and the men had no mechanical assistance – nothing but muscle power, hammers and chisels to hack their way into the solid limestone rock. The tunnel they cut was roughly 1.75 metres wide – so three men could just stand side by side; and 1.75 metres high – so they could just stand upright. In practice there were probably two men working on the top half of the rock face, kneeling on the bench or step they left untouched, and two more – also on their knees – a metre behind them, hacking away the bench. No doubt there were two or three others removing all the rubble that was produced. Carrying this back to the mouth of the tunnel would clearly be more and more of a chore as the tunnel progressed.

After perhaps a year the men had bored their way some 200 metres into the rock. Then Samos was threatened by Persian enemies, and Eupalinos decided to speed up the process. But there was a real problem. If he set more men to work next to those already in the tunnel they would cut a wider tunnel, but they would not go forward any faster. The only way to complete the project more quickly was to dig at the same time from the other side of the mountain, but this raised a triple problem there. How high up the mountain should they go? Where should they start? And in which direction should they dig? They found the answers with the application of pure geometry, although exactly how is still a matter of debate.

Amazingly, after some five years of digging, the two tunnels did meet in the middle of the mountain. Modern surveys show that if both sides had kept going in straight lines they would have been close to meeting head-on, but in practice they seem to have got nervous. The team tunnelling from the north worried that they were too low, and turned sharply upwards. As a result, when the tunnels met the floor of the northern one was almost 2 metres higher than the one coming from the south; it was overshooting it altogether. The tunnellers had to cut the floor down to make a passage between the two.

Also, as they approached each other both teams turned sharply towards the east. This may have been because each thought it was going in the wrong direction; but it may also have been a clever fail-safe manoeuvre to make sure they would not miss one another completely. With one tunnel headed south-east and the other north-east, they could not miss as long as they were on the same level. The result was that when the tunnels met they did so almost at right angles.

In both tunnels the floor is almost horizontal. Eupalinos – or perhaps one of his minions – seems to have made some unfortunate errors here. Perhaps he thought that because water flowed enthusiastically from the spring it could be carried right through the mountain in horizontal pipes; why else did they make the tunnel floor horizontal? In practice, you need a slight downhill slope, of perhaps one in a hundred, to keep water flowing freely. This is about the minimum gradient used in Roman aqueducts and by competent plumbers today.

On the other hand, as modern engineers have pointed out to me, tunnellers never want to tunnel downwards – water always seeps into tunnels; if they go downhill the tunnel will gradually fill up, and they will soon be working under water. So with the benefit of hindsight it might have been better to start from the south side of the mountain, perhaps 10 metres lower than the end of the existing tunnel, and work slightly upwards, towards the spring.

The conduit taking the water from the spring to the mouth of the tunnel seems to have been progressively steepened to get the water to flow properly. As a result, the clay pipes carrying the water were more than 3 metres below the tunnel floor at the north entrance. In order to get the water to flow through the mountain a deep ditch had to be dug in one side of the floor. Its depth gradually descends from over 3 metres on the north side to about 9 metres on the south side. Digging this colossal ditch in solid rock must have needed at least as much work as cutting the 'service tunnel' above. Nevertheless, the Samians managed this Herculean task; clay pipes were laid in the bottom of the ditch, and eventually fresh spring water flowed in abundance into the city.

Pythagoras and proof

Sadly, the water may well have come too late for a lad called Pythagoras, who was born on Samos in about 570 BC, but probably left the island a few years before the tunnel was built – although the southern city is now named after him. He sailed to southern Italy, and set up a marvellous, mystical, mathematical college or brotherhood at Croton, under the ball of Italy's 'foot'. The school was run with strict rules. Among other things, its members were not allowed to wear woollen clothes, touch white feathers, eat beans or 'make water in the sunshine'.

For Pythagoras and his followers, everything was to do with numbers. Numbers ruled the universe. **One** represented the beginning of everything, **two** the earth, **five** the wind or colour, **six** cold, **eight** love, and so on. Sadly, the brotherhood did not write things down, and its members were sworn to secrecy; so our knowledge of them is sketchy. However, it is likely that he understood triangle numbers and square numbers; he probably worked out their relationships not by using symbols but with pebbles in the sand.

It is known that Pythagoras loved music, probably set up the musical scale that is used in the West today, and believed that the gaps between the heavenly bodies were in proportion to the harmonic intervals – and so began the notion of the harmony of the spheres.

The story goes that he was wandering past a blacksmith's shop and heard the hammers ringing on the anvils, with different notes. Investigation soon showed that the note depended not on the strength of the hammerer but on the size of the hammer and the anvil. He experimented by plucking a string stretched on a wooden frame, and found he could get a higher note if he shortened or tightened it. When he tried two strings, one half the length of the other, he got two notes that were different, but sounded similar, and harmonious. Today we would call the second note the octave of the first. This is probably, roughly, how he sorted out the musical scale.

We remember Pythagoras for his famous theorem, which says that in any right-angled triangle the square on the hypotenuse is equal to the sum of the squares on the other two sides. This relationship had been known for hundreds of years, but he proved that it was always true. In fact, his most important contribution was to establish the concept of mathematical proof.

When Rabbi Lionel Blue was asked on the BBC radio programme *Desert Island Discs* what book he wanted to have on his desert island, he replied that he would like to have something that he knew was true, so he would choose a volume of pure mathematics. Proven mathematical theorems are among the only things in the universe that we can be certain about. Mathematical proof is absolute.

The best-known of all the Greek mathematicians was Euclid, who lived in Alexandria in about 300 BC. He hoovered up all the known mathematical ideas, invented more of his own and wrote them all down as propositions with proofs, in a vast multi-volume book called the *Elements*. Euclidian geometry survives to this day, and Euclidian proofs are elegant exercises in logic.

Proof provides one of the important distinctions between science and mathematics. In mathematics proof is everything, and mathematicians will work for years, even hundreds of years, to find proof for a proposition. Science, by contrast, can never prove that anything is true, but only that some things are not true.

When scientists want to know the cause of a phenomenon they make a guess at possible explanations. Then they try to use the guess to predict what will happen next, or the outcome of a new experiment. If their prediction turns out to be correct, this is good evidence that the guess was correct, but does not prove it is right. The more predictions that come true the better the evidence – yet it takes only one or two that are seriously wrong to disprove the theory.

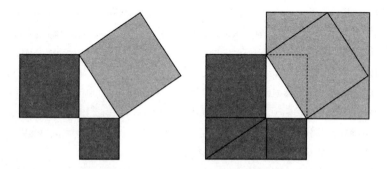

Pythagoras proved that in any right-angled triangle the square on the hypotenuse is equal to the sum of the squares on the other two sides. The figure on the right shows a geometrical proof of the theorem.

Science in ancient Greece was based on observation and argument. The most respected scientist was Aristotle, a pupil of the philosopher Plato. Plato did not do experiments, and said the best way to advance in science was to set clever men arguing; if they were clever enough and argued for long enough they were sure to find the truth. Aristotle was born in 384 BC and spent much of his life in Athens, apart from the years when he was tutor to the young man who would become Alexander the Great. He made superb observations of such events as the development of an embryo inside a chicken's egg. He was arguably the last man to write down all the existing knowledge, in the areas of politics, ethics, philosophy, and science, but he was less interested in mathematics.

One of my favourite examples of applied mathematics was carried out by Eratosthenes in Egypt who, in about 240 BC, measured the size of the earth. When Napoleon ordered his surveyors to do this in the 1790s the task took them eight years, and even then they made a mess of it; but Eratosthenes used a stroke of mathematical genius – a coup of practical Euclidian geometry, since geometry, derived from Greek, means earth measurement.

Eratosthenes noticed that when he looked down a deep well on Elephant Island at Syene (now Aswan) in the south of Egypt, at noon on midsummer's day, he saw a reflection of the sun in the water. Since the surface of water is always horizontal, the sun must have been exactly overhead, and a stick pushed vertically into the ground would have no shadow. We would now say that Elephant Island lies on the tropic of Cancer.

The port of Alexandria lies 800 km (500 miles) to the north. Eratosthenes knew the distance because trained army pacers (*bematistoi*) had marched there from Syene counting their steps. He pushed a stick vertically into the beach at Alexandria at noon on midsummer's day, measured the length of the shadow and worked out that the sun must be one-fiftieth of a circle away from the vertical – equivalent to 7.2 degrees in our units.

Then came the stroke of genius. If the distance from Syene to Alexandria corresponded to one-fiftieth of a circle, the whole circle – the circumference of the entire earth – must be 50 times 800 km (500 miles); that is 40,000 km (25,000 miles). This is almost exactly right. Eratosthenes actually measured the distance in *stades*, but there were several different Greek *stades*, and no one knows which one he was using. So we can't be sure just how accurate he was – but we do know he was astonishingly close, especially as the instruments he used were so simple.

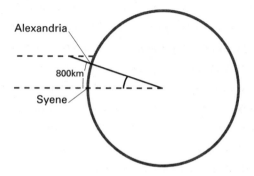

Eratosthenes compared the lengths of shadows cast by the sun under the same conditions at Syene and Alexandria to determine the fraction of the earth's circumference represented by the distance between those two places, and thereby calculated the size of the earth.

Eratosthenes was also a skilful poet, a literary critic, librarian at the famous library of Alexandria for 40 years, and a famed mathematician who, among many other things, invented a way of finding prime numbers known as the Sieve of Eratosthenes.

A wonder of the world

The Greek colony in Alexandria represented almost the final flowering of Greek culture. The city was founded by Alexander the Great in 322 BC, towards the end of his amazing conquest of most of the known world. He realized that if it was to flourish it would need a safe haven for ships, but in the delta of the Nile there was no rocky inlet, no natural harbour to give protection from storms. So he gave instructions for two huge construction projects.

A mile offshore lay a tiny islet called Pharos. Alexander told his men to build a curving mole or breakwater to the island, so that there would be a protected anchorage behind it; in other words, the mole would create a harbour.

In order to mark the position of the new harbour on the featureless coastline, he gave orders to build a lighthouse on the islet, tall enough to be visible from far out at sea. His men toiled for many years and constructed a fantastic stone tower some 90 metres high, the tallest lighthouse the world has ever known. On top, beneath a bronze statue of Poseidon, was an open fire so that the tower could be seen by night as well as day, from 60 km (40 miles) out to sea. Inside there was probably a simple lift to keep the men at the top supplied with firewood.

The designer of this huge structure was an engineer called Sostratus, and according to legend he had his name inscribed on the stone, but tactfully covered it over with mortar and carved a tribute to the current king, Ptolemy. His plan was that the mortar would eventually wear away, revealing the name of the real builder for posterity. And it worked. Many years later Pliny the Younger wrote: 'I cannot but note the singular magnanimity of king Ptolemy, who permitted Sostratus of Knidos to engrave his own name in this building.'

Unfortunately the tower – one of the Seven Wonders of the Ancient World – was destroyed by an earthquake in 1302, and has been replaced by an imposing fort called the Citadel. However, the lighthouse achieved immortality. Built on the little island of Pharos, it became known as the Pharos and derivations of this name have been used as words for lighthouse in many languages, including French (*phare*) and Spanish (*faro*).

Mathematics and technology

A contemporary and friend of Eratosthenes was Archimedes, my superhero and perhaps the greatest mathematician and scientist in the ancient world. He lived in Syracuse on the island of Sicily in the third century BC, and his great love was for mathematics.

He wrote a book called *The Sand Reckoner*, in which he tried to work out how many grains of sand it would take to fill the universe. To do this he had to invent a whole new system of counting, because the standard Greek method could not handle numbers big enough to describe the problem. And he sent Eratosthenes an amazing puzzle about cows, which would have taken a whole book to solve.

In his entire life, the feat of which Archimedes was most proud was working out that if you fitted a sphere inside a cylinder, so that it touched both ends, both the volume and the surface area of the sphere were exactly two-thirds those of the cylinder. He asked for a diagram of the sphere in the cylinder to be engraved on his tombstone and, sure enough, the Roman writer Cicero found it 200 years later.

Archimedes was obsessed by mathematics, often to the exclusion of normal life. Some three centuries later, his Greek biographer Plutarch wrote that he was so 'bewitched by a Siren who always accompanied him, he forgot to nourish himself and omitted to care for his body; and when he was urged by force to bathe and anoint himself, he would still be drawing figures in the ashes or with his finger draw lines on his anointed body.'

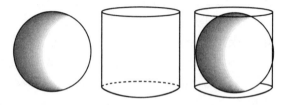

Archimedes calculated that the volume and surface area of a sphere is exactly two-thirds those of the cylinder that just contains it.

Surprisingly, therefore, his most famous revelation happened when he went to take one of his rare baths – in the public bath house, since people did not have baths in their houses in those days. The tyrant Hieron had given a goldsmith a weighed lump of gold, and commanded him to make a wreath or fancy crown for the gods. When the wreath was delivered, someone suggested the goldsmith might have stolen some of the gold and substituted an equal weight of silver.

Hieron demanded that Archimedes should investigate and find out whether the wreath was pure gold, or whether the maker had cheated by putting some silver into it – but, naturally, he was not to melt it down. Archimedes was worrying about this as he got into the bath, and then noticed some water had slopped over the side. He had a flash of inspiration. If the bath had been exactly full, when he got into it the volume of water that spilt out of it would have been exactly the volume of his body, which had pushed the water out.

He was so excited he shouted '*Eureka!*' (I have found it), leapt out of the bath and ran all the way home, wreathed in bubbles and smiles. There he made up two lumps of metal of exactly the same weight as the wreath, one of pure gold and one of pure silver. Then he filled a bucket with water and lowered the lump of silver into it on a piece of string so that some water overflowed. Then he pulled out the silver, took a measuring jug, and carefully measured the amount of water that was needed to fill the bucket to the brim once more. This was the volume of the silver.

Then he repeated the process with the lump of pure gold, and discovered that its volume was much less than that of the silver. Finally, he lowered the fancy wreath into the refilled bucket, and when he pulled it out he discovered that it had displaced more water than the lump of gold. In other words, its volume was greater than it could have been if the wreath had been pure gold; it must contain some silver.

Thus Archimedes proved that the wreath was not pure gold, and the wreath-maker probably paid a heavy fine.

Thinking further about objects immersed in water, Archimedes realized that he himself floated in the bath, but his strigil (dirt scraper) sank to the bottom. Fruit and vegetables are interesting. Try some experiments yourself: oranges and bananas usually float, while tomatoes and potatoes sink; what about apples?

Archimedes's overweight daughter
Felt light when she swam in the water.
    'Hey, Dad, this is great!
    I'm sure I've lost weight,
Even though I ate more than I oughta.'

    'My dear, from the truth you have drifted;
It's just that you feel uplifted.
    And the uplifting force
    Is equal, of course,
To the weight of the water you've shifted.'

In other words, when a body is immersed in water it experiences an upthrust equal to the weight of water displaced. This became known as Archimedes' principle, and it explains why huge steel ships can float provided they have enough space inside, even though steel is much denser than water.

This is essentially a mathematical idea, but Archimedes also excelled at technical and engineering solutions to problems. He is credited with inventing a helical pump – simply a screw rotating inside a pipe, which can pull water upwards as far as is needed. Archimedes' screw is wonderfully simple technology. It has been used to pump water out of mines and from the bilges of ships, and for irrigation; and it is still used today, for getting water out of the Nile and for pumping sewage in Britain.

In 212 BC the Romans, under their general Marcellus, attempted to invade Syracuse but were driven back by the cunning defence machines Archimedes built. One was a sort of crane or 'claw' that grabbed the bow of an invading ship and lifted it out of the water, so that the stern was submerged and the vessel foundered when it was released.

Even more dramatic was his solar ray gun, which could set fire to a Roman ship before it even reached the shore. Apparently Archimedes had a large array of mirrors – probably polished bronze shields – each of which could be angled so that it reflected the sun on to the ship. They acted like a concave mirror, concentrating and focusing the sunlight. The sun is strong in Sicily, and the ray gun must have been immensely powerful.

The Romans used to park their warships on the beach, which kept them dry and therefore light and fast. And the planks of the vessels were made of softwood, painted with wax-based paint to keep the water out. This combination of dry wood and wax is highly inflammable – so even though some experts say it is impossible, I reckon there is a chance Archimedes could have set fire to a Roman ship.

Even if the timber would not ignite, there were the sails. And there was the captain. Suppose you were about to invade a city and the enemy on its harbour wall unleashed a ray gun that blinded your captain. You might suddenly remember several pressing reasons for turning round and going somewhere else. Roman discipline was legendary, but even the Romans might have been unsettled by such a fearsome weapon.

According to legend Archimedes died prematurely, a victim of his beloved mathematics. When Marcellus finally got into Syracuse he sent a soldier to find him, for he had immense respect for the ageing genius. The soldier discovered Archimedes poring over a mathematical diagram in the sand, and ordered him to come and meet the captain. Archimedes said, 'Hang on a minute; let me just finish this maths problem.' But the soldier was impatient, and stabbed him to death.

What is more likely is that Archimedes was killed in the general slaughter that ensued when the Romans conquered the city.

A more dramatic and memorable death was achieved by another Greek philosopher who had lived on Sicily three hundred years earlier. Empedocles was roughly a contemporary of Pythagoras, and lived among the stunning Greek temples at Agrigento. It was he who suggested that everything was made from just four elements – earth, air, fire and water – in varying proportions. Aristotle used this idea to explain the behaviour of things: they all want to get home to where they belong. So drop a stone and it falls to earth; blow bubbles in water and they rise into the air. Flames burn upwards because the fire wants to get to the sun, and so on.

Empedocles proved that air is not nothing by a simple experiment – he pushed an upturned bucket into water, and showed that it did not get wet all the way up the inside.

The juiciest story about his death goes that he wanted to demonstrate that he was immortal. So he took his followers up the mighty volcano Mount Etna, and jumped into the smoking crater. He was never seen again – but he is remembered to this day, so in a sense he did indeed make himself immortal...

Organs, clocks and robots

Meanwhile, back in Alexandria, a hotbed of Greek brilliance was flourishing. In the third century BC a barber, inventor and engineer called Ktesibios (pronounced Tessy-bee-os) appeared. He was a great maker of gadgets, and in his father's barbershop he fixed up a counterweight on a rope over a pulley, so that a heavy mirror could easily be held behind a customer's head. To keep the weight out of harm's way he fitted it into a vertical tube.

When his father raised the mirror and the weight dropped, Ktesibios noticed a squeaking noise in the tube as the weight pushed the air out. Intrigued by this, he began doing experiments, and found he could vary the note of the squeak by varying the length of the tube. Gradually he developed the idea into a water organ, which

The klepshydra *(which means 'water thief') was used to measure time in court. The upper pot was filled to the brim, with the hole in the bottom plugged. As the defendant rose to speak the plug was removed, so that the water began to escape. He or she was allowed to speak until all the water had run out.*

became known as the *hydraulis*. Water was used to compress air, often under a heavy bowl placed upside-down in a tank of water. The air was then forced out through the organ's pipes, and the instrument was played with a keyboard (see plates, page 10).

Water organs became enormously popular across the Mediterranean, partly because they were loud and could therefore be played in noisy public places. The Romans pinched the idea, as they so often did with Greek inventions, and fell in love with the sound. The *hydraulis* was Nero's favourite instrument, and was regularly played to accompany gladiatorial combats. But what did it sound like? At the end of the nineteenth century French archaeologists uncovered two stone slabs at Delphi. They turned out to be musical scores, and written on the nearby wall was an inscription that commemorated a musician called Antipatros 'covering himself in glory' by playing the water organ for two days straight in a competition.

Ktesibios also invented the force pump – which was essentially a development of his organ and was later used by the Romans in their fire engines – and superb water clocks. One place they needed to measure time was in court. Common practice was to allow defendants to speak for a fixed maximum length of time. To measure and show this a simple timing device was used. It was called a *klepshydra* (water thief), and was in fact a pot with a hole in the bottom. When an accused man defended himself the pot was filled with water before he started, and he was allowed to speak until it had run out.

This was fine for showing a fixed time, but not much good as a clock for general purposes. The rate at which the water ran out depended on its depth in the pot, so the outflow slowed down as the pot emptied. Ktesibios got around this problem by arranging that the pot was always full to the brim so that the water ran out at a constant speed. It ran into a second pot, cylindrical in shape, where a float could be used to show the time. Clocks like this were surprisingly accurate, and were not bettered for several hundred years.

Measuring time was trickier in those days than it is today, because the Greeks divided the period between sunrise and sunset into 12 equal hours. The hours were therefore longer in summer than in winter, and indeed varied from day to day. For ultimate precision you would need 183 clocks, since each one would be precise on only two days each year. This is probably why Ktesibios's clocks, although immensely ingenious and often accessorized with alarms and mechanical tricks, showed only hours and not minutes.

Following in the footsteps of Ktesibios was Hero, or Heron, of Alexandria, who lived in the first century AD. He had a superb knack for devising gadgets, and many of his devices are still of interest today; indeed we are surrounded by modern versions of them. Hero made the first vending machine: a dispenser of holy water. Put a coin in a slot, and a slurp of holy water came out of a spout at the bottom – ideal for the busy commuter on a quick trip to the temple.

Hero also made the first steam engine – really a toy to demonstrate a principle. Sometimes called the *aeolipyle*, it was a suspended bronze drum or cylinder that spun round when steam, supplied from a boiler below, was squirted out of twin tangential nozzles (see plates, page 10). Some of today's lawn-sprinklers work on the same principle – the force of the water being sprayed out causes an equal force pushing the sprinkler head round in the opposite direction. Hero's steam engine was never intended to be anything more than a toy; it has been calculated that if he had scaled it up to do as much useful work as a man, four men would have been needed to keep it running.

Another table-top model that Hero built was a 'magic' trick to open temple doors. When the priest lit a holy flame on the altar it heated air in a closed container from which a hidden pipe led to a reservoir. The increasing air pressure pushed water out of the reservoir and into a bucket. The added weight in the bucket, acting through a pulley system, opened the doors of the temple. The counterweight idea was an extension of Ktesibios's mirror-height adjuster, but using gravity in the form of falling weights became a Hero speciality.

Perhaps Hero's most spectacular machines were automata or robots, which trundled across the floor and did various tricks. In particular, he made an entire theatre in which various puppet-like characters appeared and performed a play on a miniature stage. All the action was driven by falling weights on strings, some of which were deliberately left slack at the beginning to introduce delay so that one character would finish its performance before another began.

Robots were mentioned by Homer in the *Iliad*, written hundreds of years earlier; in this the god of craftsmanship and metallurgy made intelligent, golden maidservants who helped with the housework in the palace. And Jason and the Argonauts came up against the giant bronze warrior Talos, who looked after the gold of the gods. Hero may have been inspired by these stories, but what is clear is that most of his automata were only toys, designed not to do any real work, but merely to amuse and amaze.

Bows and catapults

In weaponry, the first advance on the simple bow was the belly-bow or *gastraphetes*, which was like an ordinary bow but stronger, and could be drawn only by leaning your weight on it. It was much more powerful than a conventional bow.

The next big step forward, precisely described by Philon, was the torsion catapult, which first appeared in 340 BC. It looks like a big crossbow, mounted on a tripod, but the construction is different. The bowstring is connected to the outer ends of two separate arms. The inner end of each arm is buried in a twisted bundle of pre-stretched rope or, preferably, animal sinew, which is highly elastic.

The bowstring is then pulled back inch by inch, using a pair of levers – this mechanical assistance is necessary because the pull is so powerful – and a ratchet ensures that it cannot spring back. The string is hooked by a piece of metal shaped like a pair of fingers (which would hold a normal bowstring), and when it is fully drawn back the bolt is laid in a groove in front of the bowstring, the weapon is aimed and the shooter pulls the trigger.

These catapults could hurl a heavy iron-tipped bolt, or a large rock, over something like 300 metres with deadly accuracy, far out-shooting conventional archers. An army equipped with this kind of artillery could expect a rapid victory against anyone who lacked the same sort of weapons. The Romans adopted the Greek designs (see page 148), and catapults dominated warfare for a thousand years.

Thank the Greeks

In spite of their fearsome weapons, the real legacy of the Greeks is intellectual and social. They gave us our mathematics, and the beginnings of our science and its applications in all sorts of technology. They invented our music, our theatre and our ideas of democracy. In other words, they laid the foundations of our civilization.

VII

THE ROMANS

Rome has been a major city for well over two thousand years, and was the capital of a major empire for several centuries before and after the time of Christ. During this time, the Romans developed many innovations in fields ranging from warfare to water engineering. Although they based much of their culture and technology on what they inherited from the Greeks, they added their own special contributions, and their cities, road networks, building techniques and machines were often strikingly similar to their modern counterparts.

Rome itself, however, was an ancient city, and the Romans dated its foundation to 753 BC. According to legend, Romulus and his twin brother Remus were orphans who were abandoned by the Tiber and suckled by a female wolf. Romulus built the new city where this had happened, on the banks of the river. In fact – less romantic – Romulus was a Latin chief who was selected as the first of a line of kings of Rome. But by about 509 BC, the Romans had had enough of kings – especially Tarquinius Superbus, the tyrant who ruled at this time – and decided to throw them out and found a republic.

Rome flourished as a republic and began to conquer its neighbours. In the second and first centuries BC the Romans amassed a huge empire that stretched right around the Mediterranean. By the time of Christ, they ruled most of Spain, France (Gaul), Italy, Greece, western Turkey and much of the eastern Mediterranean and North African coasts. They later added areas such as Germany and Britain. To hold on to these vast and far-flung lands, they needed a powerful army.

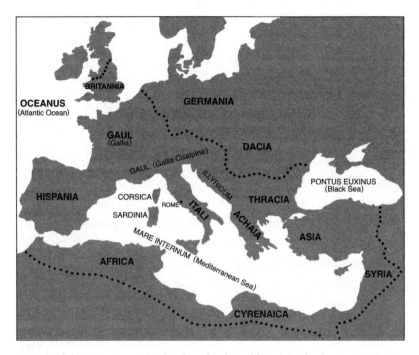

Extent of the Roman empire (within the dotted lines) in the first century AD.

A war machine

The Roman army was by far the best-organized fighting force in the ancient world. Under the great general Marius, who professional-ized it in about 100 BC, it was divided into units of fixed numbers of men – legions of 6000, divided into 10 cohorts of 600, each made up of six 'centuries' of 100 men. The soldiers were properly kitted out in a uniform (not that common at the time), consisting of metal and leather armour that protected them in battle.

Their weapons included a dagger, a sword and a *pilum* – a heavy javelin about 2 metres long with an iron point attached to a wooden shaft. The point could severely injure or kill a man and could also get stuck in his shield, rendering it useless and its owner helpless. Cunningly, just behind the point the shaft was made of soft iron.

If a soldier hurled his *pilum* at an enemy but hit a rock, the tip would bend, which made the weapon much less dangerous if his opponent picked it up and hurled it back.

Roman soldiers were well trained in the use of their weapons. They went on regular route marches carrying all their equipment – around 30 kg (65 lb) of it – and were drilled in all sorts of manoeuvres and formations. Perhaps the most famous of these was the *testudo* (tortoise), in which a group of men closed ranks to create a solid wall of shields. The front rank held the shields in front of themselves and the rest of the troops held them overhead, to make an impenetrable barrier that protected the soldiers even when arrows rained down on them from above.

So the Roman legionaries were true professionals, and probably the first fighting force to combine the best available equipment, training and fighting techniques. For a while, when the empire was growing, they were virtually unbeatable.

Their invincibility was partly due to their advanced military technology, and they probably got the idea of large-scale siege weapons from the great Macedonian general and emperor

The testudo, *or 'wall of shields'. Pity the poor man who had to steer!*

Alexander the Great, who besieged cities with them during the fourth century BC. The Romans used battering rams to knock down city gates, while catapults and stone-throwers could damage the walls, send defenders plunging to their deaths and make everyone in the legionaries' line of fire tremble with fear. Perhaps the most frightening of all was the deadly accurate, arrow-firing *ballista*, which could kill with precision at a range of 300 metres. All these, the forerunners of modern artillery, were developed and improved by the Romans from the original Greek designs (see page 144).

The Romans used these weapons on a huge scale. At one siege during the Galilean war in the first century AD, the emperor Vespasian had 160 artillery weapons arranged in a circle around the town of Jotapata. These were fired in a controlled barrage, overwhelming the men on the walls with arrows, firebrands and showers of stones. Stone-throwers were also used in the siege of Jerusalem. At first they were not very effective, because the shiny white stones could easily be seen. Lookouts spotted them as they were launched, shouted 'Baby on the way!' and the city's defenders had time to duck. When the Romans realized what was happening they blackened the stones, making them less easy to spot. And they began to hit their targets.

Roman catapults, like their Greek precursors, worked by the power of torsion springs. They developed various versions; one, the onager, was apparently named after the wild ass (onager) because it delivered a mighty kick. Its throwing arm had a sling, designed to hold a stone. The arm was held between twisted bundles of rope or, preferably, sinews. The operator needed to use enormous force to pull back the arm, and when he let it go it moved at great speed, launching the stone high and fast towards the enemy. But the weapon did have its problems. Aiming was not easy – you had to be the right distance away and it was necessary to get just the right degree of elevation to ensure you hit the enemy fair and square. Not only that, but there had to be perfect coordination between the men who operated the catapults and the rest of the force, so that the attackers could take the best advantage of the destruction caused by these weapons. This meant bringing in the battering rams with speed once the defenders were knocked for six, so that the city gates could be demolished without the legionaries coming under too much fire. One answer was to build a device that combined a catapult and battering ram, an ingenious dual-purpose weapon described by the writer Apollodorus in the second century AD. Despite these heavyweight siege engines, it was probably the *ballista* that was most effective in Roman battles.

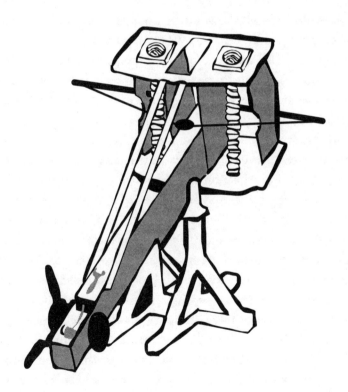

The Roman catapult, or ballista, *was developed from a Greek design and could shoot iron-tipped arrows with deadly accuracy over a range of at least 300 metres.*

Road-building

Rome amassed a huge empire, which kept its army in continuous active service, though by no means always in battle. The legions spent a lot of their time off the battlefield, building the infrastructure that was needed to keep the territory that had been conquered – and rule it efficiently. To do this, the Romans developed the most advanced engineering skills of their time. Everywhere they went they put up strong forts, built to a standard design. They were skilled at building even larger fortifications, such as the 120 km (75 miles) of Hadrian's Wall that marked the northern boundary of the empire. But above all, they were famous for their roads.

They needed roads to get their troops around the empire quickly and efficiently, and to enable officials and messages to travel at speed from one place to another. Roads were important also for transporting goods, because the Romans needed to keep their legions supplied, and also wanted to exploit the products of their conquered territories as much as possible.

So the army built the best roads it could, planned on a huge scale. Whereas, previously, muddy tracks had developed in an ad hoc, disorganized way, the Romans devised an entire system of roads, connecting major cities and ports across the whole empire. It was the world's first international road network. Many of today's roads still follow the Roman ones, mainly because of their straightness, the way they take the shortest route from one city to the next. The Romans used their mastery of surveying techniques to build roads that were often perfectly straight for dozens, and sometimes hundreds, of miles.

They could make them straight because their surveyors used a simple but clever instrument: the *groma*. Again probably Greek in origin, this was a sighting device that consisted of a horizontal, wooden crosspiece held on a stand. A plumb bob dangled on a string from each of the four ends of the crosspiece.

Suppose a surveyor wanted to find a straight line between two points, A and B, which had a hill between them so that he could not see

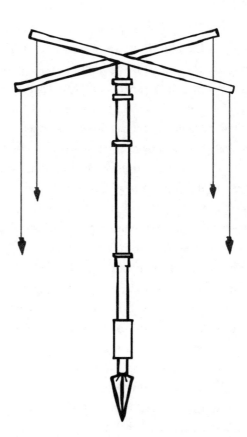

The groma, *a sighting device that consisted of a cross-piece mounted on a pole, was almost the Roman surveyor's badge of office. This instrument enabled him to build straight roads and square forts.*

directly from one to the other. He would go to the top of the hill, stick his *groma* in the ground, and turn the crosspiece until he could sight along two adjacent strings and line them up with A. Then he would walk round the *groma*, without moving it, to see whether the strings lined up with B. If not, he would move along the hilltop and try again, repeating the process until the same two strings lined up with both A and B. Then he knew he had a straight line, and could instruct soldiers to plant stakes along the route, lining them up by eye.

Using their *gromas*, a team of surveyors could line up a row of beacons on hills along the planned direction of the road. In this way they could survey a straight route for tens of miles across the country. Then the hard work of digging and building could begin.

The roads were incredibly well made; so well, in fact, that in some places we can still see where the original surface has survived. This applies to the most famous of all Roman roads, the Appian Way, which links Rome to southern Italy (see plates, page 11). The obvious thing about the sections that survive is that they are paved with close-fitting polygonal flagstones, to give a hard, weatherproof surface – a far cry from the muddy tracks people were used to before the Romans came. The road is also cambered, so that water runs off easily into the ditches on either side. This means it remained usable in bad weather, enabling troops to march south at speed and enforce the power of Rome all the way from the capital to Brindisi.

What is not obvious from the surface is that the Appian Way also has solidly built foundations. Roman engineers normally specified a good layer of stones laid in rows to give a solid base, followed by a generous layer of sand, or a sand-and-gravel mixture, on top of which they laid the surface. This was often made up of pebbles compacted together, sloping on either side of the road to a drainage ditch. Flagstones, as on the surviving sections of the Appian Way, were sometimes used, especially for city streets, and kerb stones were also often provided.

The Appian Way is still impressive. And it was well used, as is shown by the wheel ruts that have been ground into the flagstones over the centuries. It was a vital artery for the Romans. Not only did it allow them to take their rule to southern Italy, but from Brindisi it is only a short sea journey to Greece, which they soon took over. So they quickly learnt that roads led the way to expanded territory and the riches of conquest.

In any large empire good communications are vital, and the Romans set up an efficient postal service, with couriers galloping along the roads to deliver messages to and from the governors of provinces. Relay stations where they could change horses (or stay the night) meant a courier could travel up to 240 km (150 miles) in a day.

Daily bread

The well-trained, hard-hitting Roman army could move around the empire at speed, but to be really effective it had to be well provisioned – Julius Caesar would have agreed with Napoleon that an army marches on its stomach. And Caesar knew that food was vital for everyone, not just his troops. The Romans had no rice or potatoes, so their staple food was bread; and Caesar thought he would keep people happy and content under Roman rule if he distributed a free grain allowance to every citizen.

This seemed like a good idea, but there was a problem. Many city-dwellers in the empire lived in cramped apartments without proper kitchens. They had no facilities to turn grain into bread. The answer was large-scale commercial bakeries where the richer members of the population could buy bread. (The poor could eat wheatmeal porridge, which could be made with unground grain and cooked quickly over a fire.)

Making bread is hard work. First, the grain needs to be ground to produce flour, and to turn the heavy millstones the Romans used donkeys or waterwheels if possible. Kneading the dough is also labour-intensive and there is evidence, although it is not conclusive, that the Romans developed a kneading machine. A carved relief on the tomb of Eurysaces, a baker in Rome, shows all the activities involved in producing bread, from taking delivery of the grain through to baking and then weighing the loaves, and to having them checked by the imperial officials.

At the kneading stage of the relief is an image of a device that looks like a cylindrical container with a post coming out of the top. An animal appears to be harnessed to the post, to turn it just as millstones are turned at an earlier stage in the process. The device has been interpreted as a kneading machine, in which wooden paddles would have been attached to the post to turn and aerate the dough. If this is the case, the Romans invented a precursor of today's posh bread-making machines.

Bread wasn't the only kind of food Romans bought. They could also buy hot snacks, in the form of patties rather like modern-day hamburgers, at the many bars on city streets. So you could say they pioneered fast food in Europe (see page 101). In spite of the great gulf in time and culture, the Roman empire and the Western world today have in common a fast-moving and city-based lifestyle; and plenty of people without the time and patience – or perhaps the skill – to cook elaborate meals.

The Roman games

Roman emperors knew a good food supply was one way of keeping the people contented. But they also realized that good entertainment was another palliative; so they invented games to keep the population amused. These came in various forms: chariot races, mock sea-battles and, most famous of all, fights between gladiators. In Rome itself there were several places where games were held. The long racetrack known as the Circus Maximus, an enormous structure, was the place for chariot races. Gladiators fought in the arena of one of the best-known buildings in the empire: the Colosseum (see plates, page 12).

The Colosseum was a great oval nearly 200 metres across, with terraced seating rather like a modern football stadium, and 50,000 people could watch the games, which sometimes involved thousands of gladiators. The combatants often fought to the death – although the audience had the right to show mercy by stopping the fight before the final death blow was delivered.

To make the games more interesting there were various kinds of gladiator, distinguished by their differing armour and weapons, and one type fought another in often bizarre pairings. The *secutor*, for example, fought with a straight sword called a *gladius* (from which the word gladiator derives). He was usually pitted against a *retiarius*, who was armed with a trident and a large net in which he could catch his opponent like a fish. Other gladiators included the Thracian, who had a curved sword rather like a cutlass, and the *myrmillo* who, like the *secutor*, fought with a *gladius* but had it tied to his wrist with leather thongs.

When they were not fighting each other, some of the combatants were required to fight animals – especially lions or bears – that were brought into the arena from cages in the basement by means of special lifts. This shows how clever and complex the Colosseum was. Below the raked seating was a network of arches and vaults that held the whole structure up. Passages leading to the 80 doorways allowed the huge crowds to get to and from their seats with minimal delay. And there were cells for the gladiators, and cages and lifts for the animals. Altogether this building was a major feat of engineering.

The action took place in the large central arena – a word that comes from the Latin for sand, which covered the floor and soaked up spilt blood. The floor itself could also apparently be made watertight, which enabled the arena to be flooded for the staging of mock sea-battles, another amazing example of the lengths to which Roman rulers went to keep the people entertained.

Glorious glass

Like visitors to a modern tourist attraction, people who went to the Colosseum often chose to round off the experience with the purchase of a souvenir. Among the most popular mementos of a day at the arena were glass beakers, usually adorned with the pictures and names of popular gladiators. These beautiful little vessels (see plates, page 13) show how they were revered – in much the same way as modern premiership footballers. They also show the Roman skill in another important technology: glassworking.

The ancient Egyptians had been skilled glassworkers, and the Phoenicians of the eastern Mediterranean were famous for their glass wares. But the Romans took the material to new levels, and archaeologists commonly find glass containers (or fragments of them) on Roman sites. All sorts of shapes and sizes were made, from small perfume bottles to large drinking vessels. The Romans were skilled glassblowers, and made many of their pieces by blowing into preformed moulds.

Their products were often coloured or murky, because early glass was full of impurities which produced a rich palette of colours. Much of it is greenish, and some has a beautiful rainbow-like iridescence. But the Romans eventually discovered how to exclude the impurities and make clear glass.

This had all sorts of advantages. For one thing, Romans were great wine drinkers, and you need clear glass to appreciate the colour of wine. And it was also good in windows – most people in the empire made do with ones that were shuttered, but some could afford costly glass so that they could see out and still keep the heat in. There is even evidence that some Roman buildings were fitted with double glazing.

The clear Roman glass opened up exciting possibilities for the future. No one could have made effective lenses and mirrors, and the host of useful items that contain them, without glass that was perfectly clear.

Bath time in the empire

Glass was especially useful in the windows of public baths, which were some of the most important and well-used buildings in the empire's towns and cities. Crowded city apartments lacked bathing facilities, so Romans went to the public baths to get clean. But the baths were for more than hygiene. They were popular meeting places where people could go to relax and meet their friends.

A session at the baths was not a case of a quick wash and brush up. You took it slowly, using not just a bath but a whole suite of rooms. The first was the changing room, where you put your clothes in a locker. From there you went to the *tepidarium*, or warm room, where the floor was heated and you might have a wallow, or just sit and gossip.

The next stop was a hot room, with the walls as well as the floor heated, where you might take some light exercise to warm up your muscles. Beyond this there was sometimes an even hotter room, where you could build up a prodigious sweat. In one of the hot rooms you covered your skin with olive oil and one of the attendants scraped it, and any dirt, off with a curved metal scraper – a strigil. After that, you might have a massage, and then jump into the cold plunge pool. You might even repeat the circuit before returning to the changing room and your clothes.

This whole process depended on the *hypocaust* (central heating system). Roman builders constructed a low cellar under the floor of the bath house, supporting the floor above with short columns. A furnace heated the water for the hot pool and, at the same time, the air in this subterranean void; soon the floor of the bath house was warm – or sometimes hot enough to force bathers to wear slippers. Smoke and fumes from the furnace were also drawn up through flues or chimneys embedded in the walls (see plates, page 12). The

Roman bathers applied oil to their skin to draw the dirt from the pores, and used a strigil, a curved metal implement, to scrape it off.

flat, clay flues soon warmed the walls, which were covered with marble on the inside. The result: sweltering central heating.

In due course rich Romans fitted *hypocausts* in their own homes, both to heat private bath houses and to warm their other living accommodation. Central heating was especially common in large houses in Britain, the most northerly and coldest province of the Roman empire. Archaeologists are still discovering villa sites with *hypocausts*, and the rows of short columns that supported the floors of the hot rooms are a familiar sight to visitors to places such as Fishbourne in West Sussex and Chedworth, Gloucestershire.

Roman *hypocausts* were both simple and ingenious, like many successful inventions. But they depended on a large population of slaves, who were needed to keep them running. Shovelling fuel into a furnace in the cellar of a bath house must have been exceedingly unpleasant in the blistering heat and choking smoke – because the aim was to keep the heat in, there was very little ventilation. The slaves had little choice but to put up with all this; no respectable Roman would give up his or her habit of keeping clean and meeting friends at the public baths.

Running water

A Roman bath complex needed one other obvious resource: a good supply of water. Some of the ones in Rome and other major cities were huge, and very few had a natural spring like the one at the famous baths at Bath in England. So piping in water became a major concern for the Romans. They also needed water to drink as much as anyone else, and their empire included many dry areas around the Mediterranean. So their skilled engineers set to work, and built long aqueducts to get water to the centres of population where it was needed.

Roman aqueducts are familiar to many people because of the huge stone structures with rows of arches that take water across valleys. One of the most spectacular is the Pont du Gard at Nîmes in

France (see plates, page 13), and there are others from Spain to Syria. These are superb structures, showing how Roman builders mastered the use of the arch in a way that was foreign to most of their predecessors. But aqueducts involved much more than arches – long pipes, channels and tunnels that ran, sometimes for scores of miles, across the countryside had to be constructed.

Rome itself had no fewer than 11 aqueducts, one of which was begun by the emperor Caligula, but completed by Claudius. Called the Aqua Claudia, it is 69 km (43 miles) long and the historian Suetonius praised it for bringing into the city 'cool and copious water sources'. It can still be seen today, running on arches raised above the ground for around a quarter of its length. This channel, the eighth to be built, improved the city's water supply, but the Romans wanted even more. So they built a ninth aqueduct, which for part of its course runs in a channel directly above that of the Aqua Claudia. This is the Anio Novus, at 85 km (53 miles) the second longest of all Rome's aqueducts. By putting one channel on top of the other, the Romans saved the immense cost of building another set of arches. Eventually, Rome's 11 aqueducts could carry 38 million gallons of water to the city every day.

Aqueducts travelled more discreetly, underground, for most of their course. This kept them safe from damage, from wind or erosion, kept the water clean and cool, and also hid them from view so that they were less vulnerable to attack by an enemy. This was important, because poisoning or cutting off the water supply was an attractive tactic for besiegers who wanted to force a city to surrender.

The stonework of both the raised and underground sections of the aqueducts is impressive. But what is even more amazing is the precision with which they were built to give exactly the right slope.

An aqueduct has to slope gently down towards its final destination so that the water flows freely. If it is too level the water stagnates; if the downward slope is too steep the water flows too fast, increasing the risk that it will overflow at bends after heavy rain, in the short term, and eventually erode the stonework. So Romans became skilled at maintaining a slight, steady gradient in their water channels. At Nîmes the channel drops on average just one-third of a metre for every kilometre it travels. This gradient, 1 in 3000, is low even for the Romans, who were happy to range between this and 1 in 200, which is roughly the lowest that plumbers use today.

Just as important as the supply of fresh water was getting rid of sewage with a minimum of fuss. Most Roman homes had minimal sanitation, but settlements all over the empire were famous for their public lavatories. These, with their rows of keyholed stone benches, provided as little privacy as the public baths. Indeed, the users must have sat shoulder to shoulder, since the holes in many surviving latrines are only about 60 cm apart. The lavatories seem to have been places for social chatting, like public baths, and were in fact usually built next door to bath houses whose waste water could be used to flush them.

Lavatory paper had not been invented, and Romans seem to have used sponges on sticks. These were probably rinsed after use;

Roman public lavatories were a perfect place to enjoy a chat.

ABOVE *Chinese lacquer-ware. This Yuan dynasty cosmetics box dates from the fourteenth century AD.*

LEFT *A Chinese junk, with its flat-bottomed hull, depicted in a seventeenth-century painting.*

ABOVE *This picture of court ladies preparing newly woven silk was itself woven into a piece of Chinese silk, using coloured inks and gold thread, early in the twelfth century.*

The Greeks

LEFT *The Antikythera mechanism is unique. This bronze contraption, which measures about 30 cm (12 in) in diameter and dates from the first century BC, was discovered on the seabed in 1900. It puzzled the experts for more than 50 years, until X-ray analysis revealed its complex inner workings and enabled the American archaeologist Derek da Solla Price to work out that it is, in fact, an analogue computer for predicting the movements of the planets.*

ABOVE *The* hydraulis, *or water organ, was invented by the Greeks, but later adopted by the Romans. This Roman mosaic shows a water organ being played to accompany a gladiatorial contest.*

RIGHT *Model of the toy steam engine invented by Hero of Alexandria in the first century AD. Steam from the boiler passes up one of the hollow legs and jets out of two nozzles in the drum suspended above, making it spin.*

LEFT *The Appian Way, the most famous of all Roman roads, links Rome to southern Italy. The Roman army built the first international road network to move troops and transport goods around their huge empire quickly. Many modern roads follow these ancient routes.*

BELOW *The remains of two large ships built for the emperor Caligula in the first century AD were recovered from the bottom of Lake Nemi, south of Rome. They provide evidence that the Romans used ball bearings to reduce friction – 1500 years before Leonardo da Vinci came up with the idea. This modern reconstruction shows how these bearings were positioned to smooth the movement of rotating platforms like capstans, the purpose of which is not known.*

ABOVE *The Colosseum in Rome, the largest of all Roman amphitheatres, was opened by the emperor Titus in 80 AD.*

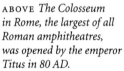

RIGHT AND ABOVE *Roman baths depended on central heating systems called* hypocausts. *A furnace in the basement heated the water for the baths, while the smoke and hot gases escaped under the floor and up narrow flues in the walls, keeping the rooms wonderfully warm.*

ABOVE *The 270-metre-long Pont du Gard aqueduct in France is a masterpiece of Roman civil engineering. The Romans created superior concrete using* pozzolana, *a volcanic ash, which enabled them to build many ambitious structures, including arches and domes, that survive to this day.*

ABOVE *The Romans took glassmaking to a new level of excellence, eventually developing ways of removing impurities to make clear glass for drinking vessels and windows.*

The Arabs

ABOVE *Astrolabes enabled Islamic astronomers to determine the altitude of heavenly bodies, measure the heights of mountains and calculate time. This copper example is 12 cm (5 in) in diameter and was made in Iraq in the ninth century.*

LEFT *This tessellating pattern of coloured tiles is on a wall in the baths of the harem at the Alhambra at Granada, Spain.*

ABOVE *The Blue Mosque in Istanbul, Turkey, was built between 1609 and 1616. Islamic buildings are often highly decorated.*

The Mesoamericans

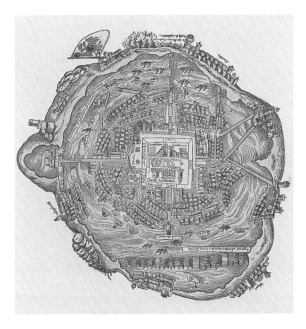

LEFT *Tenochtitlan, the capital city of the Aztecs, was one of the ancient world's largest cities, with a population of hundreds of thousands. This map appeared in a letter to Emperor Charles V of Spain from Hernan Cortes, the Spanish invader who besieged and then destroyed the city in the 1520s.*

BELOW *The colossal stone heads produced by the Olmec people are thought by some to depict rulers wearing helmets for the ritual ball game.*

ABOVE *The Mayans used three complicated calendars at the same time. This one from Yaxchilan dates from the eighth century.*

BELOW *Ballcourts were a feature of Olmec ceremonial centres. In the games held at these venues teams of players used their hips and shoulders to keep a rubber ball aloft.*
RIGHT *The Incas recorded information using a complex arrangement of coloured and knotted cords known as a* quipu.

ABOVE *The Aztecs believed that human sacrifice was needed to enable the sun to rise each day. Those who died in battle, in childbirth or on the temple altar went to the heaven of the sun god. It was an honour to be chosen for sacrifice; to nourish the gods and sustain the world.*

but the idea of using someone else's cannot have been appealing, and it seems likely that people carried their own sponge sticks with them.

In Britain until 1800 sewage ran out into the public roadway, where it joined other waste thrown out of houses. This caused a health hazard and a stink. But in ancient Rome there was a main sewer, the *cloaca maxima*, which discharged into the Tiber, and helped to keep the city clean and healthy. Surprisingly, Romans failed to make any connection between sewage and disease, even though contamination of drinking water has probably been the world's biggest killer. They built the *cloaca maxima* just to get rid of the smell.

The Romans certainly enjoyed their running water. As well as lavatories and baths, Rome boasted many fountains and ornamental water-works. This must have given it an air of luxury – in most ancient towns of southern Europe water was such a precious resource that it would have been irresponsible to squander it on such things.

However, there was another practical side to water usage: in industry. Running water is a valuable power source, and in some places the Romans developed the waterwheel to power grain mills.

This was yet another invention that the Romans probably pinched from the Greeks, but they were among the first to realize the waterwheel's true potential and combined it with gears to build powerful watermills. An outstanding example was at Barbegal in France, where no fewer than 16 waterwheels drove 16 mills to grind grain, a factory-like complex that must have amazed contemporaries. There was a similar multiple-wheel mill in Rome.

In fact, work and pleasure came together in Rome; under the vast baths of Caracalla there were mills driven by run-off water from the baths themselves. Flour from these was used by on-site bakers to produce bread for the bathers – and some scholars have speculated that the ovens may have been heated by the bath's

The Romans developed water as a power source for industry. In Barbegal, France, 16 waterwheels drove 16 mills to grind grain.

furnaces. Whether or not this was the case, the baths with their mills are a notable example of two enterprises benefiting from each other – and supplying their customers with two quite different amenities.

The first power saw?

Mills were common in the Roman world, but water power may have been used to drive other kinds of machinery. There is a tantalizing hint in some lines by the Gallo-Roman poet Ausonius, who was writing in the fourth century AD. He refers to a river 'turning the mill-stones with rapid, whirling motion, and drawing the creaking saws through smooth white stone'.

Until recently there was no archaeological evidence for a sawmill that would fit Ausonius's description. But in 2000, archaeologists began to look closely at a late-Roman building in Jarash, Jordan. This was obviously the site of a waterwheel – there is a pair of cisterns that supplied a head race and a wheel race. Clearly visible in the latter are rectangular holes which must have taken the bearings of a wheel shaft. There is also evidence, in the form of circular wear-marks on the nearby stone, that wooden wheels were fitted to either end of the shaft. There is no evidence of any millstones, and the arrangement is different from that of a typical grain mill.

Also found on the site were two partly cut stones, each of which has groups of four saw slots, which match each other and look as if they were made mechanically. It seems likely that whatever machinery was attached to the waterwheel was used for sawing slabs of stone.

No one can be sure exactly how the machine worked, but it is unlikely that Roman technology was capable of producing circular or wire saws; so the likelihood is that there were reciprocating blades that moved forwards and back again like an ordinary handsaw.

For this to work, the machine would have needed a device to convert the circular motion of the waterwheel into reciprocating motion. The most probable mechanism was an eccentric and connecting rod in which wooden wheels on either end of the shaft would have been pierced near their edges with a pin, linking each to a rod that moved back and forth as the shaft rotated, powering the saws. The result – a powerful to-and-fro motion that would have been ideal for cutting blocks of stone for building into slices of a standard size and shape.

This is conjecture; it is not known for sure whether Romans had a machine like this. And the mill is very late in the Roman period –

the best guess is that it dates from the sixth century, the time of the emperor Justinian who ruled from the city of Constantinople (modern Istanbul). This was a period of much building work, when emperors liked to line the interiors (not just of bathhouses, but of palaces and churches too) with thin slabs of marble. So advanced stone-cutting technology would have met their needs perfectly. The water-powered saw of Jarash is a strong possibility, and there may well have been others scattered around the empire.

On a roll

Another piece of evidence of Roman skill with machines was discovered in some luxurious ships that belonged to the first-century emperor Caligula. The find reveals that the Romans seem to have known how to use ball bearings to reduce friction – something not described until the writings of Leonardo da Vinci some 15 centuries later.

According to historians, Caligula built some extraordinary boats – long galleys that were kitted out with amazing luxuries such as bath houses and banqueting halls, all decorated with inlays of precious stones and fine woods. For hundreds of years, people thought that descriptions of these vessels were exaggerated, but in the early twentieth century the remains of two such boats were discovered and recovered from the bottom of Lake Nemi, a crater lake some 32 km (20 miles) south of Rome.

When the two vessels were raised, people were amazed. Both were around 70 metres long – far bigger than any other ships of the ancient world. And their on-board luxury lived up to Caligula's decadent reputation; there were mosaics and marble decorations, statues, and hot and cold water carried in lead pipes. They may have been pleasure craft, or they may have been part of one of Caligula's religious cults. Either way, the Romans eventually got tired of the emperor's excesses; he was notoriously extravagant and even planned to elevate his favourite horse to the office of consul. So they put Caligula to death and removed all traces of him. By accident or design, the ships sank to the bottom of the lake.

Their size and luxury was remarkable enough. But the remains of the vessels also revealed technological secrets. There were anchors with movable jaws, of a type not seen again until the eighteenth century. And there were ball bearings, which were used to help smooth the movements of rotating platforms like capstans. No one knows how these platforms were used, but the ball bearings indicate that the Romans had worked out how to reduce friction, hundreds of years before such bearings became common in machines.

Building to last

Roman skill with machines was more often put to practical use, as it was with the mechanical saw. Another example of this was the crane, the ancestor of today's cranes on construction sites the world over. But the most impressive Roman building innovation was not a machine but a material: concrete.

Concrete is a mixture of cement and aggregate – gravel or stones – which slowly sets to a rock-like mass when it is wetted. Most people think of it as a modern material, but several of the structures already mentioned in this chapter, such as the Colosseum and the aqueducts, would have been impossible without it. Used in combination with the arch, which the Romans preferred to the straight lintel used by the Greeks, it could produce incredibly strong structures. In fact, it is thanks to concrete that many of their buildings still exist today.

As with other innovations, the Romans did not invent the material; there is a concrete floor in the Balkans that is around 5000 years old. However, they were able to develop and make much use of it because they discovered a magical ingredient: *pozzolana*.

Pozzolana is a sandy volcanic ash found in the Pozzuoli area of the bay of Naples. Romans marvelled at this material because they noticed that when it came into contact with sea water it set hard, forming a strong, stone-like mass. This cement was both strong and waterproof, and so was as good for the construction of bridges and harbour walls as it was for buildings on dry land. Not until after the 1750s, when John Smeaton did a series of experiments, did Britain acquire waterproof cement.

The Romans were soon using concrete with *pozzolana* in all kinds of structures. In towns like Ostia, the old port of Rome, where hundreds of buildings still stand, practically every one is made of this material. It may not look this way at first glance, because the concrete is often faced with brick. But it is there, under the surface, lending the buildings great strength, and allowing Romans to build tall structures. Major cities in the empire had many apartment blocks of four or five storeys – the world's first high-rises.

In the first century AD Vitruvius, the great Roman writer of the builder's manual *On Architecture*, described how to mix *pozzolana* with lime and rubble, and recommended the material especially for maritime works. But Roman builders appreciated its strength in all sorts of buildings. In fact, the concrete core was often stronger than the bricks used to face it, and in some places it has survived while the bricks have disappeared.

Another advantage of concrete was that it was possible to create many different room shapes – builders were not limited to the squares and rectangles that come most naturally when bricks or regular blocks of stone are used. The material was ideal for vaulting, giving a smooth finish to the undersides of curving barrel vaults, arches and domes, all of which the Romans liked to use in large and important buildings. Structures like the Pantheon in Rome would have been impossible without concrete.

The huge, unsupported dome of this great circular temple benefits from an extra bit of Roman cunning. For the aggregate in the concrete, its builders used not ordinary gravel or pebbles but lumps of volcanic pumice stone, which is honeycombed with holes and so much less dense than ordinary rock. The result is that the dome is much lighter than it would have been if it had been built with normal concrete.

Thanks to *pozzolana*, Roman harbours like Trajan's near Ostia were bigger, and better built, than those of previous eras. And Romans were also good at using the material to build the uprights of bridges. Vitruvius explains how to do this by making a coffer-dam and pouring the concrete in so that it forces the water out. The presence of water is no problem if the concrete is made with *pozzolana* – the material just sets rock hard. A number of Roman bridges survive to show its lasting strength, and some even carry modern traffic.

Concrete was also used in conjunction with arches, which were invaluable to the empire's builders. They were not invented by the Romans, but no previous culture used them as widely. An arch is both stronger and more elegant than a lintel, and enables quite complex free-standing buildings to be constructed. For example, Greek theatres were fan-shaped structures set into hillsides. With the aid of the arch and concrete, Romans could build ones of a simi-lar shape that were free-standing.

Concrete enabled the Romans to build on a large scale, and, for them, size mattered. They had a huge empire, a vast road network, long aqueducts, an enormous army and big buildings. In order to achieve all this they needed to be incredibly well organized and have an almost endless source of labour. This quality of organization, seen so clearly in the Roman army but also evident in their network of roads, the grid-planning of their cities, their postal system, and their layers of local and imperial government, is what makes them especially remarkable. It is the unseen invention, the guiding princi-ple, that makes everything else they did for us so effective.

VIII

THE ARABS

In the year AD 610, there was an event that changed the world for ever. A merchant called Muhammad, from Mecca in the Arabian peninsula, had a series of revelations during which he claimed a voice spoke to him, using the words of God himself. These words were later written down as the Koran, the sacred book of Islam. At the heart of their message is the belief that there is one God, and that all mankind should submit themselves to him. Muhammad had become the prophet of a religion: Islam.

In the next couple of decades Muhammad attracted a large following, and by the time he died in 632 most of the people of the Arabian peninsula were followers of Islam. They chose a series of caliphs, or successors, to carry on Muhammad's work, and these men became both religious and military leaders who conquered an enormous area of the globe. By 750, the Islamic empire stretched from Spain all the way across North Africa to Arabia, Syria, and Persia, stopping at the river Indus in modern-day Pakistan. It lasted for several centuries – for example, Spain's Muslim rulers finally left the country in 1492. But even after the empire broke up, Islam remained the dominant faith in the Middle East and in many other parts of the world.

The people of the Islamic empire were well educated, because everyone was expected to learn Arabic so that they could understand the Koran in the actual language in which it had been revealed to Muhammad. As well as schools in which children learnt its words by heart, there were higher-level ones, called madrasas, where students read and discussed the text. Muhammad himself saw the significance of knowledge and education, and one of his sayings is 'The quest for knowledge is obligatory in every Muslim.'

Still higher studies were pursued at universities and at the famous House of Wisdom in Baghdad. This was founded in 830 by the caliph al-Ma'mun for the specific purpose of translating ancient Greek books – especially those on philosophy and science – into Arabic.

This was unprecedented. The Koran is almost unique among major religious books in encouraging the study of science. The faithful are urged to observe such things as the flight of birds and the falling of rain, and this endorsement of scientific study had a lasting effect on the unravelling of the secrets of nature. A side effect of the old and new ideas being written in Arabic was the incorporation of many Arabic words into science and technology. Thus al means the, and we still use this prefix in alchemy, alcohol, algebra, algorithm, alidade, alkali, alkaloid, altitude and many other words. However, there is a difficulty, in that Muslims were not all Arabs, and Arabs were not all Muslims; so the material in this chapter is part Arab, part Muslim and part both.

The Muslim scholars knew that it was vital to find out what scientists from other cultures had discovered, and one famous

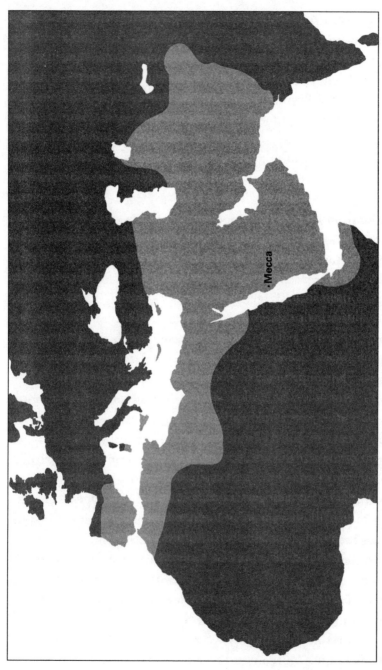

By 750, the Islamic empire stretched from Spain, across North Africa to Arabia, Syria and Persia, all the way to the Indus.

saying instructs them to 'seek knowledge, even unto China'. When Muslim armies conquered new territories, scholars or scientists went with them or followed them. For example, a number of military raids on northern India carried Islam to the Punjab and took the scientist al-Biruni to the area. Al-Biruni learnt Sanskrit and discovered much about the work of Indian scientists and geographers. In a similar way, the conquest of Egypt and Syria brought Muslims a knowledge of scientific discoveries made in these two areas. Scholars combined wisdom from the Greeks, Indians and Chinese with what they themselves had found out, and this thirst for knowledge means that some of the most important inventions in the history of technology were devised under the blistering suns of the Islamic empire in Spain, North Africa and the Middle East.

Observing the stars

The early people of the Arabian peninsula were nomads who spent their lives travelling across vast deserts, often on camels, known as 'the ships of the desert'. There were few landmarks and, like sailors at sea, they learnt to navigate using the stars; so observing the heavens became second nature. As a result, many Arabs became notable astronomers and, unlike others who based many of their ideas on untested theories, much of their astronomy was based on actual observations of the stars. With the coming of Islam this tradition continued, and was even reinforced by the Koran, which tells the faithful that God has 'set for you the stars, that you may guide your course by them amid the darkness of the land and the sea'.

Muslims were interested in astronomy for other reasons too. All Muslims commit themselves to five key tenets, known as the Five Pillars of Islam. These are the profession of faith (the assertion that there is one God and that Muhammad is his Prophet); regular prayer at set times, five times a day; almsgiving; fasting during the holy month of Ramadan; and making the pilgrimage to the city of

Mecca at least once in a lifetime. The fourth pillar meant the calendar was of key importance to the faithful – every Muslim needs to know when Ramadan occurs. So observation of the moon and stars became a key activity of Arab scientists.

One of the great astronomers of the tenth century AD was al-Sufi, who produced a catalogue, *Book on the Constellations of Fixed Stars*, in which he gave Arabic names to all the visible stars, including Aldebaran, Altair and Algol. Algol means the ghoul, and was so named because as astronomers watched it they saw it wink at them, and thought it was the eye of the devil. The same star was observed in 1785 by the 21-year-old deaf-mute astronomer John Goodricke, in York. He described it so skilfully that he was elected a Fellow of the Royal Society, but sadly died the following year. Algol was known then as a variable star, and is now called a binary star; it has a companion nearby, and they revolve around one another. The other star is less bright, and so when it gets in the way Algol appears to dim – or, in other words, it seems to wink.

Most early Islamic astronomers worked at home, although some found that the minaret of a mosque could make a good vantage point for looking at the stars. But they soon began to build observatories and equip them with impressive collections of astronomical instruments. Some of these observatories, such as the one at Maraghah in northern Iran built in 1259 and another in Istanbul established in 1575, became centres of study where many scientists gathered to look at the heavens and pool their discoveries. This resulted in organized scientific institutions of a kind not known in Europe until much later – one of the important ways in which Islamic scientists were ahead of their western counterparts.

Many new stars were discovered in the observatories, and Muslim astronomers compiled catalogues to record their findings. They also measured the movements of the planets with more accuracy than the astronomers of the classical world. Some of this was achieved by better observation in the purpose-built observatories with groups of astronomers working together in close collaboration. The advanced mathematics of the Muslim world also helped. This astronomical knowledge enabled scientists to create the best calendars and almanacs of their time. People could tell with ease which month of the Muslim lunar calendar they were in, and they knew exactly when Ramadan was approaching.

The second pillar of Islam, regular prayer, posed another challenge. Prayers have to take place at specific times of the day, so Muslims needed to know the time – but they had no mechanical clocks. To begin with, they worked out the approximate time of day by measuring the length of a shadow cast by a post. However, this was tricky and imprecise, and scholars were soon on the lookout for something that would enable them to work out the time more precisely.

One instrument in particular that helped them was the astrolabe, a device for observing the sun and stars. A primitive version had been invented by the Babylonians as a map of the heavens hundreds of years earlier (see page 40), but the Muslims turned it into a powerful and versatile astronomical calculator (see plates, page 14). It enables the user to determine the altitude of a heavenly body in the sky and it can be used to measure the height of a mountain. In addition, it allows you to calculate the time.

Most astrolabes consist of several brass discs linked to a sighting device called an alidade. One of the discs – the rete – is a map of the night sky with bright stars marked by special pointers and with the paths of the sun and planets shown. The rete is pierced so that you can see the disc behind it, and all the discs can be rotated independently. The instrument can be used to solve various astronomical problems, such as finding the time a certain fixed star will rise on a certain date, or determining when the sun will rise and set – vital for the fasting during Ramadan. During the thirteenth century professional astronomers were appointed whose primary job was to determine the times for prayer.

To make a measurement, you first hold up the astrolabe by inserting a finger or thumb through the ring at the top, so that it hangs vertically, and make a sighting of the sun or star using the alidade. You can then read the altitude from a scale around the edge of the instrument. Line up the correct pointer for the sun or star over the relevant altitude line on the disc below, and you can read off astronomical data that let you calculate the time of day.

The first people to design calculator astrolabes were probably the Greeks. The great astronomer Hipparchos described the device, and Greek scholars in Alexandria knew about it. The Muslims got interested in it when they conquered Egypt in the seventh century. Over the next few centuries they improved the instrument, developing the technique of projection by which points on a spherical surface (the night sky) were transferred to a flat surface (the disc of the astrolabe). The mathematical skills needed to do this were combined with the craft skills of the metalworkers to produce some of the most beautiful scientific instruments the world has known.

They were also some of the most useful, because once you are able to work out the time of day or night you can solve many other problems. And so astrolabes were used widely in all sorts of areas, from astronomy pure and simple to navigation; one important application was to determine the direction of Mecca, towards which Muslims face in prayer. One tenth-century Muslim scholar, Abd al-Rahaman, wrote a treatise on the astrolabe that lists 1000 uses of the instrument.

Muslim astronomers were practical men – they based their work on real observations, rather than theories. They were curious, and clever enough to wonder how we see, and did pioneering work in vision and optics.

How do we see?

Most ancient Greek philosophers misunderstood light and vision. They thought we could see because our eyes sent out some form of ray, which was intercepted by the objects in our field of vision. The ray altered the air in some way, creating a 'luminous breath' that enabled objects to be seen. Philosophers such as Ptolemy and Euclid realized that light was needed for us to see things, but they thought the light illuminating objects interacted with the 'luminous breath' from our eyes to make vision possible.

One Arabic scholar, al-Hazen – Abu Ali Mohamed Ibn al-Hasan Ibn al-Haytham – changed our understanding of vision; he has been called the greatest physicist of the Middle Ages. He was born in Basra – now in Iraq – in about AD 965. When he heard about Egypt's problems with flooding in the Nile valley, he had what he *thought* was a brilliant solution: why not dam the river? Its waters would be contained when it was in flood, and could be used for irrigation. So he wrote a proposal to the ruler of Egypt, Caliph al-Hakim.

The caliph was delighted, sent for al-Hazen and greeted his honoured guest in person at the gateway to Cairo. Finally, accompanied by workmen and a load of al-Hakim's money, al-Hazen travelled south to Syene (now Aswan) to start the great project. When he got there, and saw how massive and wide the river was, he realized there was no way he could dam the Nile. There wouldn't be anything like enough money, materials or labour.

He thought he had better admit defeat right away, but he was so afraid of what the notoriously brutal caliph might do to him that he pretended to go mad – and had to stay 'mad' until al-Hakim died 12 years later. It's a pity he couldn't have seen today's Aswan dams – concrete proof that his idea was absolutely right. After the caliph died in 1021, al-Hazen moved to Cairo, and earned his living by copying works such as Euclid's *Elements*, and by teaching. His most impressive achievement, however, was his study of the behaviour of light.

He wrote on many aspects of optics including mirrors, rainbows, the aberrations of lenses and the formation of shadows. He studied Ptolemy's writings on vision in his book the *Almagest*, and realized that Ptolemy had got it wrong. He saw that the light we need for vision is actually a physical property quite independent of our eyes – light from an object comes to you rather than being sent from your eye to the object. In other words, vision is a passive process; when you open your eyes to look at something, light bouncing off it pours into them like water pouring down the plughole when you pull out the bath plug.

In making his studies of light, al-Hazen discovered some of its most important properties: it travels in straight lines and it can be reflected and refracted – and it obeys the same rules whether the light source is the sun or a candle. What is more, he was one of the first people in the world to test his theories with experiments, establishing one of the keystones of scientific method that is still in place today.

All this helped al-Hazen to draw some remarkable conclusions about the cosmos. His research on refraction led him to suggest that twilight occurs when the sun reaches an angle of 19 degrees. From this finding, he concluded that the earth's atmosphere has a finite depth – which he estimated to be about 15 km (9 miles), whereas in fact it is nearer 30 km (18 miles). But even if his estimate was inaccurate, he was still centuries ahead of his time.

During his researches into the properties of light al-Hazen developed the camera obscura. The principle on which this is based was known to the ancient Greeks and is mentioned in the writings of Aristotle, but al-Hazen was the first to study it systematically. Originally a camera obscura was a dark, windowless room with a tiny hole in the middle of one wall. In fact, this is what its name means – camera is Latin for room, obscura for dark. Light from the world outside pours in through the hole and makes an image on the opposite wall. The image is faint, upside down and reversed left to right, but nevertheless shows the scene outside the room.

Al-Hazen showed that when three lamps were burning outside, three images appeared on the opposite wall inside the camera obscura, and that he could put his hand in the way and block any one of these at will. This was the first direct proof that light travels in straight lines – from each lamp, through the hole, to the image on the wall. He had a tent that he rigged up as a portable camera obscura, and used this to make observations of the sun, and also to demonstrate to others this apparently magical device – no one had ever seen moving pictures before. But it isn't magic; it is science. And it neatly demonstrates al-Hazen's key discoveries about light and vision.

Scientists were not alone in being fascinated by the camera obscura. Many artists of the seventeenth and eighteenth centuries used it in their work, to help them draw complex scenes directly on to canvas. Some of the greatest painters, such as Jan Vermeer in Holland, may well have used it in this way.

The principle of the camera obscura also lies behind every modern camera, which is why the device is still called a camera even though today's models are much smaller than rooms. Although modern cameras are festooned with lenses, buttons and microchips, they are still based on the idea developed by al-Hazen: they are all light-tight boxes inside which an image can be projected. So modern photographers are still benefiting from the tenth-century work of al-Hazen.

Al-Hazen gathered his studies on optics in a book, the *Kitab al-manazir* (Optical thesaurus). In it, he covers the anatomy and physiology of the eye, the properties of light, studies of reflection

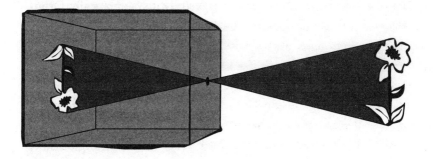

Al-Hazen developed the camera obscura. Light passing through the pin-hole at one end of the room produces a reversed, upside-down image on the opposite wall.

(especially in spherical and parabolic mirrors) and his research on refraction. He included the first known diagram of the human eye, described the function of the lens and cornea, and showed such features, and the vitreous and aqueous humours and the optic nerve. This work was immensely influential in the Arab world, and when the book was published in the West, in Basle in 1572, it was influential there too. Even Isaac Newton drew on al-Hazen's ground-breaking work in the field of optics.

Working with the environment

From Spain to the Middle East, the territory of the Islamic empire was hot and sunny, which certainly simplified experiments with light rays and the camera obscura, but brought many challenges for most people. One of the greatest was – and still is – maintaining a good water supply, both to provide drinking water for them and their animals, and to irrigate the fields. This often means moving water around, and raising it from one level to another, for example, from irrigation channels to fields.

Transporting water in a bucket is slow and back-breaking work; so in many places people used the shaduf, a bucket on the end of a pivoting pole, to make the task easier (see page 32). But one Islamic scientist came up with a solution that incorporated a piece of technology centuries ahead of its time. The scientist was al-Jazari. He lived in Diyar-Bakir (modern Turkey) in the twelfth and early thirteenth centuries, but was called after his place of birth, al-Jazira, between the Tigris and Euphrates rivers in Iraq. Al-Jazari was a brilliant engineer who worked for the local king in Diyar-Bakir, and in 1206 he produced his masterwork, *The Book of Knowledge of Mechanical Devices*. In it, he describes some 50 different machines, including water clocks, a hand-washing device and the West's first double-acting pump. Many of the designs are beautifully illustrated; he was also an accomplished draughtsman.

One of al-Jazari's most impressive machines was designed to raise water. It used a crank-connecting-rod system, the first device to turn continuous rotary movement into an oscillating, up-and-down motion. The same principle is used in all sorts of more recent machines, from the steam engine to the internal combustion engine that powers every car.

Al-Jazari's machine was based on a device now called a flume-beam swape. This was essentially a water-holding channel with a large scoop at one end, a bit like a length of gutter with a bucket stuck on to it. It was pivoted so that the scoop first dipped down into a pool of water, and was then raised so that the water flowed along the channel and out of the other end, at a higher level than the pool.

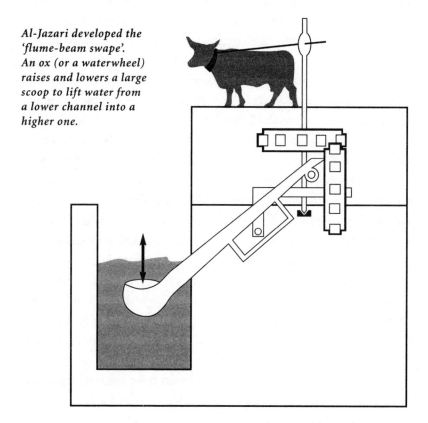

Al-Jazari developed the 'flume-beam swape'. An ox (or a waterwheel) raises and lowers a large scoop to lift water from a lower channel into a higher one.

In al-Jazari's machine the swape was lowered and raised mechanically; an ox or donkey, harnessed to a drawbar, turned a vertical axle. On this axle was a gear that meshed with another gear, this time on a horizontal axle. The clever thing was that at the free end of this second axle was a crank linked to a slot under the swape. So as the beast walked around, its circular motion was turned into an up-and-down movement by the crank, which slid along the slot, in turn making the swape rise and fall. The result was a regular supply of water raised from pool to field – without the farmer raising a finger.

What was ingenious about the water-raising machine was the way it combined various inventions. Gears had been around for centuries, and so had hand cranks, but no one seems to have thought to combine them in a machine before. And this forward-looking device was described by al-Jazari in 1206, around two hundred years before machines incorporating similar cranks and connecting rods were known in western Europe.

So the Arabs were good at coping with their dry environment, making the best use of the limited water that was available. But lack of water was a major drawback when it came to developing new power sources. Whereas European engineers developed the water-wheel to power their corn mills and other machinery, the Arabs could not, because so many of their streams were seasonal – mere trickles that dried up completely for much of the year. But although they lacked water power, they latched on to another resource: the wind. The early Muslims were among the first people in the world to develop the windmill.

In fact, the Greeks had the idea of wind power in the third century BC. The Greek inventor Ktesibios described a water organ with a pump driven by the wind, but the Greeks and Romans do not seem to have used windmills for any practical purpose.

The Islamic windmill was quite different from the ones we know in the West, where a set of sails is usually mounted high off the ground on a horizontal shaft. The sails have to face the wind, and every western windmill has some sort of device that enables the sails – or sometimes the entire mill – to turn into it.

The Islamic mill has a different design – a vertical shaft with a set of sails fixed around it. As the wind blows the shaft spins, rather like the rotating signs on many garage forecourts. This spinning rotor stands on the lower level of a building and the shaft rises through the floor to the upper level, where it turns the millstone. Down below, the walls are pierced by ducts rather like funnels, which channel the wind towards one side of the rotor so that all its force pushes the sails in one direction. The ducts are tapered, with the narrow ends pointing at the rotor, so that the incoming air is speeded up before it hits the sails. With ducts all around the mill, there is no need to turn the machine when the wind direction changes.

One great advantage of this design is that there is essentially only one moving part, as the main shaft is vertical and is connected directly to the millstone. In a western mill the main shaft is horizontal, and its movement has to be converted to rotation around a vertical shaft in order to turn the millstone. Also the sails have to be turned to face the wind, which means additional complicated mechanisms – or, on the smallest mills, a big lever sticking out of the back so that the miller can push the entire top of the mill round.

In the strong winds of the Middle East the Islamic windmill was highly effective, and its 6 or 12 fabric-covered sails could turn the heavy millstone at surprising speed. In fact, this speed was sometimes a problem – the stone could move so quickly that the grain was pulverized to too fine a powder, and the millstone itself could be damaged. So millwrights had the idea of building shutters into the sails and opening them to slow the mill down to the speed they wanted, rather like reefing the sails of a boat.

The earliest known proper description of such a mill appears in an Arabic text of the ninth century, but it refers to a Persian millwright working in 644. No one knows exactly who invented this mill, but it may have appeared in Persia or in Seistan, the western part of Afghanistan, an area without rivers. From here, windmills spread all the way around the Islamic empire, and also reached China and India. They were mostly used for grinding corn, but sometimes for other functions, for example in the sugar-cane industry in Egypt.

But how did windmills reach northern Europe? Some scholars believe wind power caught on with the crusaders, the Christian warriors who came to the Middle East to fight Muslims during the Middle Ages. When the first groups began to return to Europe during the twelfth century they may have brought the idea back with them, since the first known European windmill was established in Normandy by around 1180. By the late thirteenth century, mills were common all over northern Europe, and from there they spread to the rest of the continent as more and more millers saw the benefits of using wind power to produce flour for people's daily bread.

The Banu Musa and their ingenious devices

Devices like the windmill and the crank-connecting rod show how ingenious Islamic engineers were in designing machines. But the most ingenious of all these inventors were three brothers, Muhammad, Ahmad and al-Hasan, known as the Banu Musa (or sons of Musa), who lived in the ninth century. Their father was an astronomer and companion of the caliph, al-Ma'mun, and when he died the three boys became wards of the caliph, who had them educated at the House of Wisdom in Baghdad. After this they worked as surveyors and made a lot of money on various public building projects.

Their real passion, however, was for science and technology. Their skill in surveying and mathematics helped them to work out such things as the circumference of the earth; they checked their calculations against those of past scientists. They spent a lot of their wealth on trips to centres of scholarship, such as Constantinople, to track down scientific works by ancient writers, and paid scholars in the House of Wisdom to translate these into Arabic. But they also did a lot of scientific work of their own and are said to have written some 20 books in all sorts of different scientific fields. Only three have survived, and the most intriguing is their *Book of Ingenious Devices*.

The *Book of Ingenious Devices* contains details of 100 inventions. Some 80 are trick vessels, such as a trough that automatically refills when an animal drinks from it, and a flask from which a fixed amount of liquid can be poured each time the user tilts it. Although some of these devices derive from the work of earlier scientists, such as Hero of Alexandria, many seem to be original inventions, including a number that, like the examples above, control the flow of liquids using conical valves – devices that are still widely used in modern machines but were virtually unheard of before the Banu Musa.

Many of the inventions were meant mainly to entertain, but some have obvious practical uses that point the way to self-regulating systems that are still used today. For example, the Bana Musa describe an oil lamp that is self-feeding and has an automatic mechanism for trimming the wick. Another of their designs was a lamp with a windshield that turned automatically so that it was always facing the wind, to stop the flame from blowing out.

The self-shielding lamp was probably an invention that the brothers found useful in their work in the construction industry. This was true also of another of their devices, the mechanical grab, which may also have been used in mining. This was built in exactly the same way as a modern 'clamshell' grab, which can be used in a range of machines, from river dredgers to those fairground games in which you try to grab yourself a gold watch or a cuddly toy. The brothers' grab consisted of a pair of copper half-cylinders. When they were just above a target, such as a lump of metal ore on a river bed or a rock on a building site, the operator pulled a rope, drawing the two half-cylinders together and trapping the object between them.

Keeping clean

Some Muslim scientists went to far-flung places and developed amazing and exotic machines. But others tried to solve more mundane questions, such as how to keep clean. Islam sets a high value on cleanliness. Muslims are required to wash before prayers, so that they are ritually clean, and for this reason mosques normally have washing facilities near the entrance. The ablutions must be carried out in a set way – the hands, mouth, nostrils, ears, face, arms, and feet are all washed, and running water must be used unless it is not available. It was always clear that this was a ritual cleansing and, appropriately in the dry climate, Muslims were expected to use only a small amount of water.

But people were also expected to keep themselves physically clean. In the year 993 there were no fewer than 1500 public baths in the city of Baghdad. And this was where another Islamic invention came in useful – the Muslims were the first people to produce soap. The ancient Greeks and Romans did not use it. In the classical world people got clean by rubbing themselves with pumice stones, by spreading olive oil over their skin and then scraping it and the dirt away, or simply by washing in water. Soap remained unusual in Europe until the late Middle Ages. But in Syria soap was being made by the eighth century, and by 1200 there were many soap producers in Morocco and other parts of Arab North Africa, some of whom were starting to export their wares northwards into Europe.

One of the earliest mentions of soap-making appears in the writings of the great ninth-century alchemist and physician Muhammad al-Razi. Al-Razi, who as a physician probably realized how important cleanliness could be for human health, described how to make soap using olive or sesame oil and what he called *al-qali*. Made from the ashes of a low, woody shrub, the *ushnan*, which was found in Syria, this was about 80 per cent potassium carbonate and 20 per cent sodium carbonate, and was alkaline. In fact our word 'alkali' comes from the Arabic *al-qali*.

A recently discovered Arabic manuscript from the thirteenth century, *Inventions from the Various Industrial Arts*, gives a detailed account of how *al-qali* was used to make soap. The alkaline material, plus some lime, was boiled with sesame oil. This caused a reaction which chemists later called saponification (soap-making). The resulting sludge was then poured into moulds and left to stand until it thickened into lumps of hard soap. The result: in the Islamic world there was an easy way to keep clean, whereas in Europe people just scrubbed away with water – or stayed dirty.

Soap works because it is made up of long molecules that are mostly hydrophobic (disliking water but loving grease) but have ends that are hydrophilic (water-loving). Dirt is usually oily or greasy, from your skin, and is not easily washed away with water alone; but when you wash with soap the dirt is swallowed up by the hydrophobic coils of its molecules, leaving the hydrophilic ends free. These hydrophilic portions enable the mixture of dirt and soap to mix easily with water so that it can be washed away.

Distillation: perfume to petrol

Although they did not understand molecular processes like this, early Muslims were accomplished chemists and an important chemical process they developed was distillation. This is used today in many fields. Perhaps it is most familiar as the method by which alcohol is concentrated to produce whisky, vodka and other spirits, but distillation is also used to make perfumes, and in all sorts of scientific and industrial processes.

Muslims didn't invent alcoholic drinks – in fact, Islam actually forbids the consumption of alcohol, along with the use of mind-altering drugs. They go back much further in history – beer was the staple drink of the ancient Egyptians and wine has been made in the Mediterranean for millennia. But wines rarely reach an alcohol content of more than 16 per cent and beers are much weaker; the Arabs discovered how to concentrate the alcohol by distillation.

Distillation works because the components of any alcoholic drink have different boiling points and so can be separated from each other by heating. Spirits are produced by making a mash (of various materials – grain for whisky, for example, or sugar cane for rum) and mixing it with water and yeast. During the process of fermentation the yeast converts the sugar in the mash into alcohol, or technically ethanol, the colourless flammable liquid that forms the alcoholic part of alcoholic drinks. Ethanol boils at a temperature of 78°C, while water boils at 100°C. So when the mixture is heated the first vapour that boils off is mainly alcohol, mixed with nearly the same amount of water. This vapour is cooled to make it condense back to a liquid, which is now a simple mixture of alcohol and water, but with a much higher proportion of alcohol than before the distillation.

A device for distilling alcohol in this way is called a still. The Arabs invented various kinds, the most familiar consisting of a vessel, called a cucurbit, in which the liquid is boiled, and a cooling tube, an alembic, in which the vapours cool and condense back to liquid. There is another container, the collecting vessel, into which the liquid drips as it leaves the alembic. Numerous early Islamic writers describe distillation using apparatus like this.

If Islam forbids the consumption of alcohol, why were so many Muslim scientists interested in distillation? Well, apart from being fun to drink, concentrated alcohol had many other uses. One writer recommended using it as a solvent for medicines, another suggested using it as an anaesthetic, a third had the idea of mixing distilled wine with silver filings to produce a kind of silver ink for writing beautiful inscriptions.

But distillation can be used for all sorts of other mixtures. One of the most successful uses of the process, for which the Islamic empire became famous all over the world, was the production of perfume. Scientists distilled plant and flower material to extract the essential oils – the scented liquids that were the key ingredients of precious perfumes. The biggest centre for this was Damascus. Perfumes from here were traded all over the Islamic empire and further afield into India and China.

Perfume was produced on an industrial scale. In the twelfth century large distillation ovens containing up to 25 cucurbits were arranged in circles, one on top of the other, over a huge pan of boiling water so that they could all be heated by steam. Each cucurbit had its own alembic, which passed through the wall of the oven into the cool outside air, where vessels were arranged to collect the condensing liquid.

Another substance that was distilled was a material that we still associate with the Middle East today: petroleum. While no one had yet realized how important oil would become in later centuries, it had a number of uses as early as the ninth century. The alchemist al-Razi tells how distillers took crude oil, which they referred to as 'black naft', mixed it with white clay to make a 'thick soup' and then distilled the mixture to produce the lighter 'white naft'. This was used in various chemical processes and could also be burnt in oil lamps – the first use of the familiar fuel which now powers countless machines the world over.

An explosive mixture

Early Muslims were also involved in developing another product with awesome power: gunpowder. No one knows for sure exactly who invented it. Its introduction to Britain is attributed to the thir-teenth-century English friar, Roger Bacon, who wrote down the for-mula, in code, in Latin. However, he was only passing the information on; Muslim, Chinese and probably Indian chemists had developed gunpowder long before. The substance consisted of a mixture of three ingredients: potassium nitrate (also known as salt-petre), sulphur and carbon. The role of the saltpetre was to provide the oxygen to enable the other two ingredients to burn rapidly, producing an explosion of hot gas. But Bacon's recipe could never have produced an explosion, for it does not specify nearly enough saltpetre for the other ingredients to burn.

What probably happened was that gunpowder was first developed in China, where it existed by the ninth century AD. The Chinese had good supplies of sulphur, and of saltpetre, a chemical that was hard to find in the West. There is a general belief that they did not originally put gunpowder to military use – their main interest was to make fireworks – but in practice they were probably the first to use it in weapons; see page 94 for further details.

After finding out about saltpetre from the Chinese, Muslim chemists were making gunpowder by the thirteenth century. They created a formula very close to that still used – 75 per cent saltpetre to 10 per cent sulphur and 15 per cent carbon – and were soon developing military uses for the material. The Muslim scientist called al-Ramma, probably writing in the 1270s, compiled more than a hundred different recipes for gunpowder, for various military purposes, together with instructions for making it for rockets.

Interestingly, al-Ramma says this information was handed down from his father and forefathers, and other 'masters of the art'. This suggests that gunpowder was being made in the Islamic world at least as early as the late twelfth century and, if there were many 'masters' of the art of making it, that knowledge of this powerful substance was probably quite widespread. Shortly after al-Ramma's work, another manuscript was produced covering *The Art of Gunpowder for Serious Work and Pleasure*, showing that the use of explosives for both warfare and fireworks was well established in the Islamic empire.

By this time some westerners must have known about gunpowder, because of Roger Bacon's work. But it seems that its potential was not widely recognized in Europe, since an Arabic work of the early fourteenth century, the Beshir Agha manuscript, says the Franks – the Europeans who were leading the fight against Islam during the

Crusades – were ignorant of the art of gunpowder, and Muslims were advised to keep recipes secret from their opponents. Many Muslim writers, on the other hand, describe military uses for the material, and accounts of both small, portable cannons and larger weapons with which to attack city walls survive from the early fourteenth century.

So it seems likely that knowledge of gunpowder came from China to the Islamic empire before travelling still further west to Europe. It was Muslim scientists who developed its military use, who established the best combination of the three ingredients, and who created devices such as rockets and cannons. So they can take a lot of the credit for the huge changes that took place in warfare during the later Middle Ages, finally bringing an end to the era of the mounted knight, the swordsman and the archer.

Numbers and beauty

Their work in fields such as oil and gunpowder makes the early Muslims seem very modern, and they made advances that have benefited today's science and technology in a number of other areas. Prime among these is mathematics. One of the most important things they did for us was introduce the system of numbers that we use today, and which we still refer to as Arabic numerals. These were actually adapted from those used in India, and so were another example of the Arabs looking to the East in their search for knowledge (pages 90–92). From a European point of view, Arabic numerals are much more convenient for calculations than the Roman ones that preceded them. The Arabic system also included a symbol for zero, the lack of which was a serious flaw in Roman notation.

The Muslim contribution to mathematics went much further than this. They advanced the field of algebra – in fact, the very word is derived from Arabic; *al-jebr* means the mending of broken bones. They developed the use of decimal fractions. They were highly skilled in geometry. And they made huge advances in trigonometry, the discipline that studies the relations between the sides and angles of geometrical shapes. The exactness of their workings was phenomenal – one table of tangents created by Muslim mathematicians achieved a precision of one in 10 million.

One of the finest of the mathematicians was al-Khowarizmi. He was actually Persian rather than Arab, but went to Baghdad and became court mathematician to caliph, al-Ma'mun, whose father Harun-al-Rashid had been a great patron of the arts and mathematics and was immortalized in the tales of the *Arabian Nights*, or the *Thousand and One Nights*. In about 825 al-Khowarizmi wrote a spectacular book about mathematics, in which algebra was first described. His name has become the English word algorithm, which is a systematic procedure for solving a problem. Al-Khowarizmi collected all the mathematical knowledge he could from Hindus and included it in his writings in Arabic. These were later translated into Latin, notably by Fibonacci of Pisa, and this is how the mathematics of the ancients came eventually to the West.

Like most mathematicians who push back the boundaries of the subject, the Arabs were creative; they loved solving mind-stretching problems and making amazing patterns with their numbers. They liked magic squares – squares with grids of numbers in which each row, column or diagonal adds up to the same total. And they had a penchant for amusing problems with a point. For example, a favourite conundrum concerned the man who invented the game of chess. The ruler to whom he gave the first chessboard granted him favour and he asked for a number of grains of rice or wheat arranged on the board in a numerical sequence of squares – a single grain on the first square, two on the second, four on the third, eight on the fourth, and so on, each number double the previous one. The ruler granted the inventor his favour before someone explained to him that the total would far exceed all the grain in the kingdom.

This love of patterns had a serious side. It was rooted in the basic beliefs of Islam. Muslims believed that numbers had a sacred significance. The number one represented the unique and singular God; all the other numbers were like a ladder along which humans had to travel in order to reach him. And the beautiful patterns made by mathematics were seen as an image of divine harmony. It was therefore natural that Muslims should cover their most sacred buildings with beautiful abstract geometrical patterns – more especially so since the Koran forbids representational art (see plates, page 14).

Thus abstract patterns became the hallmark of Islamic art and remain so today. Intricate interlacings, patterns of hexagons,

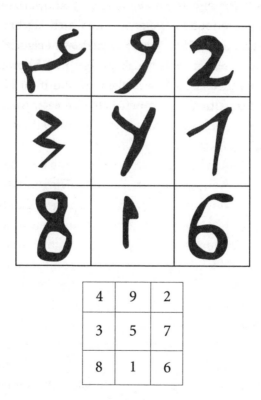

4	9	2
3	5	7
8	1	6

Arabic numerals (0, 1, 2, 3, 4, 5, 6, 7, 8 and 9) replaced Roman numerals in the West at the end of the twelfth century, but they didn't always look as they do now. This magic square, in which the numbers in every row, column and diagonal add up to 15, contains Arabic numerals as they would have appeared a thousand years ago – their modern equivalents are shown below them.

octagons and squares, continuously repeating frets, stars and circles – shapes such as these adorn mosques and other buildings throughout the Middle East and everywhere that Muslims live. Tiling – on walls, ceilings, vaults and domes – lends itself especially well to these repeating motifs; so ceramic tiles became a speciality of Muslim culture. The Alhambra in Granada, the palace of the thirteenth- and fourteenth-century Nasrid rulers of Spain, is a paradise of gardens, courtyards, fountains and interiors, all adorned with stunning patterns. Perhaps more famous still, the Taj Mahal, the tomb built in Agra, India, for the wife of the Mogul ruler Shah Jehan, is decorated with the most refined of patterns. And such designs are not restricted to buildings. They appear on virtually every other type of precious object – pottery and metalwork, wooden boxes and chests, textiles and carpets. All exploit the blend of artistic flair and mathematical understanding of symmetry that is a special product of Islamic culture, one more example of the lasting influence of the Islamic world.

IX

THE MESOAMERICANS

Mesoamerica doesn't appear on traditional maps. It is what archaeologists call, rather grandly, a 'culture area', which means that it is not a geographical region, but a region defined by the way of life of its peoples. It covers a vast area of modern Central America, stretching southeast from north-central Mexico to include most of Mexico, Belize, Guatemala, El Salvador, Honduras, Nicaragua and Costa Rica. Its rich and varied geography includes coastal strips, hot and steamy lowland jungle, savannah grassland, and cold and windy highlands.

When the Spanish conquistadores set sail for the Indies on a quest for gold in the early 1500s they found much more than that. Their galleons happened upon the coast of Mexico, home of the Aztecs, the last of many Mesoamerican civilizations that had developed over thousands of years. The history of the various Mesoamerican peoples' fluctuating fortunes is a long and complex one. The earliest Mesoamerican civilization was that of the Olmecs, who lived on the Gulf Coast of Mexico from about 1200 to 400 BC. Best known today, however, are the Mayas, whose city states were established from around 250 BC, and the Aztecs, whose empire lasted from around AD 1300 until the coming of the Spanish. But theirs were just two of a number of Mesoamerican civilizations that flourished for periods between the third century BC and the sixteenth century AD. Several other peoples, notably the Zapotecs, the Teotihuacános

Lands in Central and South America occupied by the Mayas, the Aztecs and the Incas.

and the Toltecs, came to prominence for periods in between. And although they were not Mesoamericans (for their way of life was quite different), we shall look at the Incas in Peru, whose civilization rose and fell between AD 1200 and 1532.

The pre-Spanish peoples of Mesoamerica had many things in common. Rather like the peoples of modern Europe, they spoke different languages, but had broadly similar cultures. They worshipped many of the same gods, but gave them different names. They all used digging sticks, ate maize and beans, respected the number 13 and practised human sacrifice. Interestingly, although it is known that they developed the wheel as a toy, for some reason they didn't adapt it for other purposes.

The Mayas, the Aztecs and the Incas

A thousand years before the Spanish founded their New World empire, the Mayas dominated southeast Mesoamerica, spreading over eastern Mexico, Guatemala, Belize and Honduras. The Mayas were a Stone-Age people who developed hieroglyphic writing, built imposing pyramid-temples and studied the stars with remarkable skill. But they were never politically unified. There were over 60 independent Maya kingdoms, ruled by competing dynasties and bound together by shared languages, marriage ties and competitive feasting. Each kingdom was centred on a city, and power passed from kingdom to kingdom without any one dynasty achieving permanent supremacy. The 40 or so cities of the Classic Period housed as many as 2 million people, and were supported by extensive farming systems. The Classic Period ended in approximately AD 900, but Mayan life continued, in one form or another, until the Spanish invasion. The Mayan kingdoms put up stubborn resistance, but were more or less subdued by 1546.

The name 'Aztec' refers to the groups of people who settled in the Valley of Mexico, around Lake Texcoco. The most powerful of these peoples were the Mexica. The Aztecs were the northwesterly, highland neighbours of the post-Classic Mayan peoples, and their empire ruled most of non-Mayan Mesoamerica for just over 200 years. The Aztecs were a prosperous and politically unified people with a well-stratified society, advanced agricultural techniques and extensive trade networks that stretched from the Caribbean to the Pacific. Their capital, Tenochtitlan (now Mexico City), was one of the ancient world's largest cities, with a population of hundreds of thousands. The Spanish invader Hernán Cortés defeated the Aztec empire in 1521, first besieging, then destroying, Tenochtitlan in the process. Tragically, it seems that the Aztecs may have at first mistaken the Spanish for gods returning to earth, as legend had long foretold. It was exposure to introduced diseases, such as smallpox and measles, that contributed most to their collapse. Curiously, the Aztecs were initially terrified of the sight of their invaders on horseback. Although the horse had once been native to the Americas, it had died out centuries before the coming of the Spanish, so the native peoples, who were unfamiliar with these animals, thought that each Spanish rider and his mount were a single creature!

Who, then, were the Incas? Not Mesoamericans, the Incas, in succession to other cultures, established an extensive but short-lived empire, 'The Land of the Four Quarters', in the South American Andes. Controlling most of western South America from their capital city, Cuzco (Peru), the Inca territories stretched from the northern border of Colombia to central Chile. The Incas were a devout people who dedicated one third of all conquered lands to the cult of the sun god. They never developed writing – so we cannot read their history – but tradition tells us that the first emperor, Manco Capac, founded the Inca dynasty in approximately AD 1200. Three hundred years later the empire, already weakened by civil war, came to an abrupt end in 1532 with the arrival of Francisco Pizarro and an army of just 180 men.

The Mayan calendar

Many ancient civilizations developed calendars that allowed them to record their own history, to chart astronomical observations, to plan ahead and to guide the secular and religious year. The Mayans, however, took this to extremes and used three complicated calendars at the same time (see plates, page 15).

The Calendar Round was made up of two separate calendars running in parallel:

1 Calendar one, occasionally called the *tzolk'in* calendar, had 260 specifically named days. The day names were a combination of 20 names (*Imix, Ik, Ak'bal, K'an, Chik'chan, Kimi, Manik, Lamat, Muluk, Ok, Chuwen, Eb, Ben, Ix, Men, Kib, Kaban, Etz'nab, Kawak* and *Ahaw*) and 13 numbers. The first day of the calendar was 1 *Imix*, then 2 *Ik*, 3 *Ak'bal*, and so on. Once 13 *Ben* had arrived, the next day was 1 *Ix* and then 2 *Men*. Two hundred and sixty days later the calendar would reach 13 *Ahaw*, and the cycle would start all over again. This was a sacred calendar, and each of the 260 days had its own associated omens. The Mayas took the religious aspect of time-counting seriously, combining it with astronomical observations in an attempt to predict the future. Fortunately, they wrote their observations down. The Dresden Codex (a codex is a fragile, painted book) is one of only a handful of Mayan texts that survived the Spanish conquest in readable condition. It includes almanacs, records of the movement of Venus and prophecies.

2 Calendar two was the secular, 365-day *Haab*, or 'vague year' calendar, so called because it was a vague approximation of the solar year, which is actually 365¼ days long. It is the need for an extra quarter day per year that causes most societies to insert an extra day into their calendars every four years. We in the West do this with a leap year; without this extra day we would eventually find ourselves celebrating Christmas Day in the heat of

midsummer. The Mayas did know that their calendar was inaccurate, but they did nothing to correct it. The *Haab* had 18 named months (*Pop, Wo, Sip, Sotz', Sek, Xul, Yaxk'in, Mol, Ch'en, Yax, Ak, Keh, Mak, K'ank'in, Muwan, Pax, Kayab, Kumk'u*) of 20 days, plus five unlucky days added at the end of the year. New Year's Day was 1 *Pop*, next came 2 *Pop*, and so on.

It follows that each day had two names, one taken from the 260-day calendar (e.g. 1 *Imix*) and one taken from the 365-day calendar (e.g. 1 *Pop*). The day 1 *Imix* 1 *Pop* would come round every 52 *Haabs*, or every 18,980 days, when history would effectively repeat itself.

As if this was not confusing enough, the Mayas used a third calendar, the Long Count, which was based on the *tun*, a year of 360 days. The Long Count counted forward from the end of the last Great Cycle (a period of 13 *bak'tuns* ending on 4 *Ahaw* 8 *Kunk'u*). The last Great Cycle began on 13 August 3114 BC. Specific time-periods within the Long Count calendar were named:

20 *k'ins* = 1 *winal*	(20 days)
18 *winals* = 1 *tun*	(360 days)
20 *tuns* = 1 *k'atun*	(7200 days)
20 *k'atuns* = 1 *bak'tun*	(144,000 days)

Long Count dates were always recorded in a specific order, starting with the longest time-period, so a date recorded as 10.1.19.15.17 would in fact be 1,454,357 days since the close of the last Great Cycle on 13 August 3114 BC. Check it and see (calculators are allowed):

10 *bak'tuns* = 1,440,000 days
1 *k'atun* = 7200 days
19 *tuns* = 6840 days
15 *winals* = 300 days
17 *k'ins* = 17 days

The Long Calendar, like the Calendar Round, is a repeating calendar rather than a linear one – in this case it repeats itself every 13 *bak'tuns* (1,872,000 days). This repetition hardly mattered when dating events, and fitted well with Mayan religious belief that the world had been created and subsequently destroyed at least three times.

Medicines

The Spanish were amazed at the medical knowledge of the peoples they encountered. They had a detailed understanding of the human body, including the heart and the circulatory system, and an in-depth knowledge of natural drugs. In part, this expertise developed through their religious rituals, which seem gruesome to modern eyes. The Mayas, like all the Mesoamericans, believed that blood was a symbol of fertility. They offered their own blood to the gods either to plead for special favours or as a thank you for favours already received, and they did it by using stingray spines, obsidian and chert knives, or bird or animal bones to pierce the skin and drip blood onto pieces of paper made from bark. The paper was then burnt so that the offering – transformed into smoke – could float away. Sometimes the Mayas drew blood using a cord with thorns; one beautifully carved door lintel shows Lady Shark kneeling before her husband Shield Jaguar, ruler of the Maya city of Yaxchilan. He holds a flaming torch, while she passes a thorned rope through her tongue.

The Aztecs believed that the god Quetzalcoatl sacrificed himself by bleeding to death. This led to a tradition of bloodletting known to archaeologists as autosacrifice. The Aztecs usually pierced their ears with thorns, although they sometimes also pierced the tongue, thigh, chest, upper arm and even genitals. The most devout would then put a hollow straw or reed into the hole to help draw the blood; some priests did this on a nightly basis.

Autosacrifice was important, but better by far was human sacrifice. The victim was laid on a sacred stone on top of the pyramid-temple.

The chest was cut open with a sacrificial knife, then the warm and, it was hoped, still beating heart was offered to the sun (see plates, page 16). The body then rolled down the temple steps, leaving a bloody trail, and finally the head was cut off. The victim was considered a god, and this form of death was regarded as a great honour.

The Aztecs classified their illnesses in three ways: supernatural, magical or natural. The supernatural were divinely inspired afflictions, and could be cured by an offering to the gods. Magical illnesses were the work of a sorcerer, an 'owl man', and could be treated by the consumption of appropriate cures (anything ranging from worms to skunk spray) and the possession of precious stones, such as jade. The third type of sickness, the type that interests us here, had a medical origin.

Both men and women were trained to deal with illness and injury. Female doctors tended to work indoors, so their work, being hidden, was overlooked by the Spanish, who recorded the more obvious work of the male doctors. This work was impressively practical. Broken limbs were set and held in plaster casts strengthened by splints; snake-bites were cut open and sucked free of venom; bleeding was staunched with ashes; and wounds were cleaned, first with urine (a sterile liquid used, *in extremis*, on modern battlefields) and then with the sap of the *maguey* plant, before *maguey* ointment was applied to the wound.

Maguey sap, a natural antiseptic, was just one of hundreds of tried-and-tested Aztec medicinal herbs grown in special botanical gardens. The Aztecs had anaesthetics, astringents, antiseptics and vermifuges (used to kill internal parasites). The Spanish were so impressed with the healing skills of the Aztecs that they sent their own doctors along to learn from them. Soon the Aztecs were curing the Spanish, while, in a cruel irony, they themselves started to suffer from imported diseases, such as smallpox, to which they had no natural immunity.

At the former Aztec capital of Tenochtitlan, the Spanish built a medical school. Here, in 1552, an Aztec convert to Christianity, Martinus de la Cruz, compiled a book of plant descriptions and medicinal uses. De la Cruz wrote in Nahuatl, the Aztec language. His text was translated into Latin by Juannes Badianus, and is today known as the *Badianus Manuscript*. Its 13 chapters covered hundreds of illnesses – ranging from leprosy and venereal disease to bad breath and 'rumbling of the stomach' – and hundreds of medications drawn from animal, vegetable and mineral sources. The only obvious omissions were the hallucinogenic drugs that the Aztecs used on a regular basis.

Another area in which the Aztecs excelled – and before them the Mayas – was cosmetic dentistry and tooth modification. Chewing natural gums cleaned the teeth. Healthy teeth were occasionally filed into points, or inlaid with precious stones. Small plaques of jade or turquoise were set into cavities made in the teeth using a bow drill. This must have hurt, but then the Aztecs were also experienced in the art of drug-induced pain relief.

Cocaine and tobacco

The Incas chewed all the time, mainly on the leaves of the coca plant (*Erythroxylum coca*), a domesticated plant that grew from 2 to 4 metres tall in forest clearings and on hill slopes. Coca leaves were believed to have powers of rejuvenation and stimulation, and chewing them reduced hunger pangs, allowing the chewer to work for long hours at high altitude – an important benefit in the cold Peruvian Andes. Doctors used the leaves to relieve pain, while priests chewed them to ensure spiritual cleanliness. They were burnt in special rituals so that the gods might smell their heavenly aroma and mortals might read the smoke for signs of portent. Untreated leaves had a bitter taste, but mixing them with ash or chalk softened the flavour and allowed the chewer to enjoy the secret ingredient hidden within the leaf. Today we call it cocaine.

The cocaine in the leaves is dilute, and the Incas remained healthy despite their chewing habit. But in 1860 the German chemist Albert

Neimann managed to isolate cocaine from coca leaves, and at once the possibility of addiction to the pure drug raised its ugly head. Meanwhile, in the West, cocaine was being marketed as a 'pick me up' or stimulant. A cocaine-and-wine-based elixir, *vin coca Mariani*, earned its inventor, Angelo Mariani of Corsica, a gold medal from Pope Leo XIII, who used the drink to help him relax. In 1886 cocaine was even included in the recipe of John Pemberton's new medicinal drink Coca-Cola, although it was dropped from the list of ingredients in 1903. Cocaine was used extensively by the medical profession as a stimulant, a local anaesthetic and, surprisingly, as a 'cure' for morphine addiction, advocated by Sigmund Freud.

Mesoamerica had – or thought she had – another highly prized, life-enhancing elixir: tobacco. The tobacco plant is related to some well-known vegetables, weeds and poisons, including the potato, aubergine, petunia and nightshade. Two types of tobacco existed in pre-Columbian eastern America – *Nicotiana rustica* grew in the north and was used by the Native American Indians, while *Nicotiana tabacam*, used in most modern cigarette, cigar and pipe tobacco, grew in Mexico and South America.

Today we don't tend to think of tobacco as a drug capable of inducing visions, but the Mayas did. Tobacco, known to calm the gods and bring courage to men, was used in their rituals. It was also used by doctors, who regarded it as a cure-all that would ease the diverse symptoms of asthma, nasal congestion, headaches, boils and snakebites. The Mayas dried the plant leaves, and then either chewed them or smoked them. The Aztecs, too, were keen smokers, who mixed their tobacco with crushed charcoal and then added flowers and other sweet-smelling substances.

Quinine

The Incas gave the West the treatment for malaria – and what did we give them in return? Yes, the illness itself. The anopheles mosquito, carrier of the malarial parasite, was a deadly stowaway in the Spanish galleons. Its arrival brought fevers that were treated in exactly the same way that all fevers had been treated for centuries – with bark stripped from the '*quinquina*' or *Cinchona* tree. *Cinchona* is a tropical evergreen with white or pink flowers and large green leaves. Not all the *Cinchona* family produce quinine, but those that grew on the slopes of the Andes did. The bark was either eaten freshly stripped, or was dried and powdered for later use in infusions with water and wine. Nobody knew how or why, but as the Spanish soon realized, this unorthodox and bitter-tasting treatment really worked.

In 1638, the Countess of Chinchon, wife of the Spanish viceroy of Peru, fell ill with malarial fever. She took the old Inca remedy of *quinquina* bark and was, to everyone's great surprise, quickly better. In honour of her recovery the tree was named *Cinchon*. News of the miracle cure spread quickly to Europe. Soon the bark was almost worth its weight in gold – in fact, uncontrolled harvesting of the bark very nearly resulted in the tree's extinction. The Peruvians,

Anopheles mosquitoes, inadvertently brought to South America on Spanish galleons in the early seventeenth century, introduced malaria to the continent. Fortunately, the old Inca cure of quinquina *bark, which contains quinine, was found to be effective against the disease.*

aware that they had a valuable resource on their hands, restricted the supply of seeds, but in the 1860s British and Dutch smugglers managed to obtain enough seed to establish a plantation in Java. This plantation supplied most of the world's quinine until the outbreak of the Second World War.

In 1820, French chemists J. B. Caventou and P. J. Pelletier had managed to isolate the quinine alkaloid from the bark. By now quinine was used not only to treat malaria; it could allay general fever and pain, induce contractions during labour, and act as a hardening agent in the treatment of varicose veins. It was also added to bitter-tasting soft drinks known as 'tonics', which were usually mixed with spirits. The British in India, drinking their daily G&Ts, felt their consumption justified on medical grounds, although the small amount of quinine in a glass of tonic water is actually unlikely to be effective against the bite of the malarial mosquito.

These days malaria – still a major killer in many parts of the world – is usually treated with more effective synthetic drugs, such as quinacrine, chloroquine or primaquine. However, the parasites in some areas have grown immune to chloroquine; in these cases natural quinine is, once again, the anti-malarial drug of choice.

Quipu

The Incas were a methodical and highly organized people, who understood the need to monitor the vast, mountainous area under their control. They collected and processed an impressive amount of data, including details of food shortages, census and tax information, details of mining output and records of military service. These details helped the bureaucrats to ensure the correct allocation of resources, and reduced the danger of famine. But to collect their statistics, they needed an efficient communication system. They quickly developed an extensive road network, linking together the disparate towns and villages of 'The Land of the Four Quarters'.

Unlike their Mesoamerican neighbours, the Incas had two large domesticated animals, the llama and the alpaca, both members of the camel family. Alpacas were raised purely for their wool. Llamas made good pack animals, and in a day could carry about 45 kg (100 lb) for a distance of around 20 km (12 miles), but they could not take heavier burdens and so could not be ridden. Overloaded llamas are liable to stop dead and spit at the person responsible for their discomfort! As the Incas also lacked wheeled transport, all journeys had to be made by foot, and they soon devised an efficient chain of runners to carry official communications. It is said that the Inca runners could travel from the capital city Cuzco (Peru) to Quito (Ecuador) in less time than it takes to cover that distance by car today.

But the Incas had no formal writing system, so their runners didn't carry letters, they carried *quipus*. *Quipu* literally means 'knot' in Quechua, the indigenous language of the Andes. A *quipu* is a system for coding numerical data using a series of knotted, coloured cords. It is not a writing system, nor is it a method of calculating – the Incas used counting stones, piles of beans, or a primitive abacus for their sums. But it is a highly efficient means of carrying information. A *quipu* had a thick main cord from which hung thinner cords bearing knots (see plates, page 16). The colour of the cords, the spaces between the cords, and the size and location of the knots all conveyed information to the bureaucrats known as *quipuca-mayoq*, or *quipu*-makers. It was their job to encode and decipher the *quipus*.

This sounds complicated, but is actually a relatively simple idea – rather like tying a knot in a handkerchief to remind ourselves of something. Here's an example of how it worked. Numbers were represented by knots, which were tied on the cords in units of ten and multiples of ten. The closer the knot was to the top of the cord, the higher its number. So 10,000, the highest multiple of ten known to the Incas, appeared right at the top of the cord, while 1, the lowest possible number, was at the very bottom. The number 2 would appear as 2×1 knots at the bottom of the cord, 3 would be represented by 3×1, and so on. A cord with two very high knots, and two very low knots, would represent the number 20,002.

The colour of the cord told the *quipu*-maker what was being counted. Yellow, for example, represented gold, while red represented the army. A black cord represented time, and would be used as the main cord when conveying historical data. Obviously, there were a limited number of colours available to the Incas, so colours could have a variety of meanings, just as some of our words can have different meanings today.

Early colonial writers insisted that the *quipus* didn't just contain statistics and accounting information; they also recorded epic Inca poems, legends and the history of their empire. Today we would love to read these stories, but, sadly, very few *quipus* survive. Although the Spanish courts initially accepted them as valid documents, the Catholic Church, suspicious of anything that might remind the Incas of their old religion, soon came to regard *quipus* as the work of the devil and started to destroy them. This destruction came soon after the Incas themselves burnt the emperor's *quipu* archive during a bloody civil war. The *quipus* that we have today come mainly from graves. Archaeologists assume that these are records of the goods included within the grave for the dead to use in the afterlife, but as the other grave contents have rarely been recorded, it is difficult to 'read' these *quipus*.

Suspension bridges

The Inca messengers carried their *quipus* for thousands of mountainous miles, running over well-maintained roads and stepped pathways, many of which pre-dated the Inca empire. Relay stations were provided every 2–3 km (1–2 miles). These allowed the exhausted runners to rest, and provided facilities for travellers to camp, buy food, and water their llamas.

Many of the roads crossed precarious gorges and wide ravines. No one wanted to travel around these natural barriers – a detour would add hours, or maybe even days, to an already uncomfortable journey, and would delay the official messenger system. And so the Incas developed suspension bridges that, although inclined to wobble and sag, were strong enough to carry substantial loads. The Spanish, accustomed to European stone bridges, were amazed to see bridges hanging in mid-air yet able to support the weight of their horses and cannons. The greatest bridge of this kind, the bridge crossing the Apurimac Canyon to the north of the capital city, Cuzco, spanned an impressive 66 metres and hung 35 metres above the river. It was made entirely of woven grass, yet was still being used in the 1890s, some 500 years after its construction. It owed its longevity to the tradition of annual maintenance and cable replacement by the local people.

The suspension bridge acts on the same basic principle as the washing line. Typically it is composed of cables anchored to the ground at their ends and supported by towers or pylons. The cables support the floor of the bridge. The cables are always in tension, and the towers are always in compression – this balance of opposites gives the bridge its load-bearing capacity.

The design of the Inca bridges was simple. Strong, thick, woven grass cables anchored in the ground passed over four massive stone anchors or pylons, two on either side of the ravine. The easiest way of stretching a cable across a ravine was to fire an arrow attached to a string of woven grass over the gap. A workman on the far side of the ravine would retrieve the arrow and pull the string, which would itself be tied to a thicker rope attached in turn to the cable. Four of these cables would be needed to support the bridge. With the strong cables firmly attached to the ground beyond the pylons, the workmen stretched the thinner handrail cables across the ravine using the same arrow technique. Ropes were woven and matted to make the side structure, and thick wooden branches were lashed with rawhide strips in a criss-cross pattern to the floor cables. Finally flooring mats were added. This multi-structure system of construction made the bridges strong and heavy.

Rubber

The Mesoamericans were using rubber in approximately 1600 BC, almost 3500 years before the West invented vulcanization, an industrial process that uses heat and sulphur to convert soft rubber latex into a useful, tough, elastic form of rubber. Without any need for complex chemical procedures, the Mesoamericans were able to combine two local plant products to make a useable rubber. They made hollow rubber figurines and rubber bands, which they used to tie stone tools into wooden hafts. They made waterproof shoes by brushing rubber around a foot-shaped mould. They even brushed rubber onto fabric, making the first waterproof rain capes, as re-invented by Charles McIntosh in Glasgow in 1823.

In its natural state, rubber is a latex (neither a resin nor a gum). Tapped from the Mesoamerican rubber tree, *Castilla elastica*, it is a milky-looking suspension of minute rubber droplets in a watery liquid. The evaporation of the water allows the droplets to coagulate into a tacky rubber. When mixed with liquid extracted from *Ipomoea alba*, the morning glory vine, it becomes more durable and elastic. The morning glory vine is a herbaceous climber often found growing around the trunk of the rubber tree, always twining to the right.

Raw rubber was known in Europe in the eighteenth century. In England in 1770 Joseph Priestley noted that a lump of it could be used to erase pencil marks, and because it was good at rubbing out he called it 'rubber', while in 1824 the great Michael Faraday invented rubber balloons as a way of storing the hydrogen gas that he was using for experiments. In 1839 the American chemist Charles Goodyear discovered, as a result of a laboratory accident, the process of vulcanization. Curiously, he didn't patent his discovery until 1843, eight weeks after the Scottish engineer Thomas Hancock patented the process in Britain. Vulcanization gave the West a springy, durable rubber that could be formed into precise shapes and to exact dimensions. It made an effective sealing material and could withstand enormous pressure, revolutionizing machinery design.

The latex of the rubber tree is tapped by cutting a strip of bark from its trunk and allowing the milky liquid to collect in a cup attached to it.

The world's first team game?

Rubber had many uses, but one of the more interesting was to make balls. The Mesoamerican balls bounced well – they amazed the Spanish, who had never encountered rubber before, and who lost no time in classifying the balls as Satan's toys. Nearly every pre-Columbian site of any size contains at least one ballcourt (see plates, page 16); throughout Mesoamerica there seems to have been some sort of ball game, an ancient form of football, that was both a sporting occasion and a sacred rite. It served as a substitute for warfare, as a way of resolving disputes and as a means of predicting the future; omens were read from the trajectory of the ball. Spectators gambled on the outcome of the games.

The ball game was developed by the Olmecs, the first Mesoamerican civilization, who built stone heads, up to 3 metres high, with thick lips and tight-fitting helmets (see plates, page 15). It seems possible that the helmets shown on those stone heads were worn for the game. The Mayas took up the sport and became enthusiastic players. They regarded the game as a re-enactment of the creation of the world, when twin gods, Hunahpu and Xbalenque, defeated the lords of the underworld in a vicious ball game. The largest Mayan ballcourt, measuring an impressive 94 metres long by 29 metres wide, was discovered at the city of Chichen Itza in the Yucatan.

How was the game played? Well, unfortunately, we have no rule book so we cannot be certain, but it seems that players could strike the ball with any part of the body except the hands or feet. The ball was volleyed back and forth between two sides of the ball-court, and teams lost points if they failed to return the ball correctly, or if the ball hit the sides of the court or the ground. If a player hit the ball through a stone or wooden hoop, his team won, but such goals were rare, and most games were won or lost on points. The game was rough, and the balls, because they were made of solid rubber, were heavy. To protect themselves the players wore helmets, heavy belts, hip- and knee-pads and, sometimes, a glove.

Most games were played for sport. But those that were played on ritually important days had a deadly significance. The losing side was 'honoured' by execution – they were sacrificed to the gods. The Chichen Itza ballcourt was decorated with scenes of these ritual decapitations – snakes and vines curl out of the poor victims' necks – and it seems that many of the unfortunate players ended up on the 'skull rack', a platform conveniently situated near the ball-court and decorated with images of human skulls stacked on stakes. This explains why some Mayan balls had a human skull at their centre.

The Aztecs continued the ball-game tradition, again playing to the death. To them the ball represented the sun, while the ballcourt was the dark underworld. The game became a battle between the sun and the moon, or the sun and Venus.

The floating city of Tenochtitlan

An ancient and specific prophecy told the wandering Aztec people that they must settle in the place where they saw a mythical vision enacted – an eagle grasping a snake while standing on a cactus (the eagle and the snake are today the symbols of modern Mexico). In AD 1325 the prophecy was fulfilled on a small island in swampy Lake Texcoco. Undaunted by this unpromising location, the Aztec builders set to work.

Cortés arrived in 1519. By then the imperial capital of Tenochtit-lan, home to some 200,000 citizens and closely linked to the nearby city of Tlatelolco, was ringed by exquisite gardens and fertile farm-land. Fresh water flowed in via aqueducts from nearby springs, while a lengthy dyke protected the city from the salt water of Lake Texcoco. The city was connected to the mainland by long causeways incorporating bridges. Eight major canals crossed the city, while four main roadways met in the middle. Here there were royal palaces and a ritual enclosure that included the Templo Mayor

(Great Pyramid-Temple), various lesser temples, ballcourts and a 'skull rack' designed to display thousands of skulls. Outside the ritual enclosure there were residential areas and manufacturing quarters linked together with canals and walkways. By 1522 the beautiful Tenochtitlan was all but destroyed.

The Aztecs were used to dealing with a shortage of good, flat farmland. Their hill-farmers built terraces, some of which are still used today. Their lake-dwellers used a system of *chinampas,* or artificial raised fields and islands, which they built on reclaimed swampland. This was the technique used by the builders of Tenochtitlan. Long, narrow plots were pegged out in the swampy lake-bed. Spaces were left between the plots, wide enough to allow a canoe to pass. The stakes were joined together with wattles, and the resulting fenced-off rectangle was filled with a mixture of sediment and decaying vegetation. The raised beds were deep enough to accommodate willow trees, whose root systems helped to hold the soil together, and strong enough to support huts where the farmer and his family might live. The plots could be kept under continuous cultivation, with nutrient-rich soil added as needed from the lake-bed. *Chinampas* gardens were fertilized with human waste collected from the city, and there was a thriving trade in excrement, which was sold in pots at Tlatelolco market. All this made the *chinampas* exceedingly productive, and the wild marshes provided food and animal resources – marsh delicacies, such as fish, frogs, algae, water insects and ducks – that would feed the people as they waited for their fields to take root.

Chocolate

The Mayas and the Aztecs developed a wonderfully varied cuisine. Their diet was mainly vegetarian, although they did enjoy an eclectic range of small-sized meats, ranging from turkey and iguana to frog, dog and insects, which perhaps didn't taste too bad when flavoured with the local hot chillies. The Aztecs were particularly fond of the high-protein blue-green spirulina algae that they scooped from the surface of their lakes, but the Spanish were less than impressed with this local delicacy. Both Aztecs and Mayas had a vast choice of vegetables, cereals and pulses, including maize (used to make tortillas), beans (served at every meal), tomatoes (regarded with deep suspicion by the Spanish) and sweet potatoes.

The Incas had a slightly different diet with a higher meat content, including llama, vicuna (a relative of the llama), deer and the domesticated guinea pig. Maize – roasted, boiled or made into a form of semolina – was their dietary staple, but they also ate vast quantities of beans, and they had quinoa, a grain that swells when cooked, and the potato, which they ate in the form of gruel. The Spanish were initially less than keen on the potato, which, like the tomato, is a member of the nightshade family, and they assumed to be poisonous. Some had their worst fears confirmed when they tried eating potato leaves – which really are poisonous!

Beans from the melon-like seed pods of the cacao tree were harvested, fermented, roasted and ground into a paste to make **xocolatl***: chocolate.*

Chocolate was a drink much enjoyed by the Olmecs, the Mayas and the Aztecs, who, living at high altitude, could not cultivate the plant themselves but had to acquire the cacao beans from their more fortunate neighbours by trade or through war. The Aztecs valued the hard-to-get beans so much that they used them as a form of currency – taxes could be paid in the form of cacao beans – and they restricted the drinking of chocolate to their warriors, their elite and their priests, who drank it as part of religious ritual.

Once again, the Spanish were not impressed with the new taste. In 1590 José de Acosta, a Jesuit missionary who had lived in both Peru and Mexico, described the new drink for the uninitiated:

> *Loathsome to such as are not acquainted with it, having a scum or a froth that is very unpleasant to taste. Yet it is a drink very much esteemed among the Indians, where with they feast noble men who pass through their country. The Spaniards, both men and women, that are accustomed to the country, are very greedy of this choco-late. They say they make diverse sorts of it, some hot, some cold, and some temperate, and put therein much of that 'chilli'…*

Chocolate comes from the seeds of the tropical Central and South American cacao tree, *Theobroma cacao*. (*Theobroma* is Greek for 'food of the gods'.) The cacao tree fruit is a huge, melon-shaped pod that holds 20–40 beans. The beans were harvested, fermented, roasted and ground into a paste. This could be mixed with dried flowers or spices – chilli was a popular addition – before being added to water and either shaken in a gourd or beaten until frothy. Montezuma, the last Aztec emperor, is reported to have drunk no other drink, consuming up to 50 goblets a day. He was a great believer in the restorative effects of *xocolatl*, referring to it as: 'The divine drink, which builds up resistance and fights fatigue. A cup of this precious drink permits a man to walk for a whole day with-out food.'

The Mayas reportedly worshipped the cacao tree, believing it to have a divine origin. The Aztecs knew exactly where the tree had come from. It had been brought to earth by the god Quetzalcoatl, who descended from heaven on the beam of a morning star carrying a cacao tree stolen from paradise.

The Nazca lines

High on the Atacama Desert of Peru lies one of the more baffling mysteries of the ancient world. Hundreds of dead-straight lines, some of them tens of kilometres long, are drawn on the desert surface. These so-called 'Nazca lines' are thought to have been the work of the Nazca Indians, the precursors of the Incas, and include huge pictures of animals and birds, including a spider, a monkey and a hummingbird.

Making these lines is easy; you just have to move aside the dark stones on the surface and expose the pale yellow soil below. And experiments have shown that people can lay precisely straight lines for considerable distances simply by using sighting poles. Similarly, geometrical figures and animal pictures a metre or two across can be scaled up by finding the centre and then multiplying the distance to each point. But the burning question is why would anyone want to go to the trouble of making the lines? The Swiss archaeologist Erich Von Däniken suggested that they were runways for spaceships. The German mathematician Maria Reiche said that the lines pointed to the rising and setting positions of sun, moon and stars, although this has been disputed. Or perhaps they connected small hills in the desert, or pointed to ancient water sources. The jury is still out.

A further question is why are the figures so huge and the lines so long? The only way to see them clearly is from the air. Were the Nazca Indians able to fly in hot-air balloons, as some have suggested? Or were they making these pictures and signs for their gods above? We may never know the answers.

Thank the peoples of Mesoamerica

Hardly any of us is untouched daily by the innovations of the Mesoamericans, who certainly knew how to make the most of their environment. And cigar-smoking, chip-eating, cocaine-addicted, malarial, chocoholic rubber fetishists everywhere have particular cause to raise a glass of gin and tonic to these ingenious peoples.

INDEX

Page numbers in *italics* refer to maps and illustrations

ACKNOWLEDGEMENTS

My thanks go to the many people who helped with writing this book, especially Joyce Tyldesley, Keith Laidler, Philip Wilkinson and Graeme Grant. Thanks also to the publishing team at BBC Books – Sally Potter, the boss; Christopher Tinker, my editor; Ian Bilbey, who drew all the illustrations; copy-editors, Tessa Clark and Vicki Vrint; designer, Ann Burnham; picture researcher, Deirdre O'Day; and Sarah Reece, who checked the proofs – and the entire BBC TV production team who made the programmes – executive producers, John Farren and Martin Mortimore; director, David Coleman; series producer, Ian Potts; producers, Will Aslet, Jane Cameron, Martin Kemp, Liz Tucker, Patricia Wheatley, and all their assistants and production managers; not to mention the many academic experts who helped in all sorts of ways – especially Irving Finkel, Tracey Rihll, Sir Crispin Tickell and Michael Wright – the Screenhouse team who built all the props; and my fellow presenters, Amani Al-Aidroos, Jamie Darling, Hermione Cockburn and Marty Jopson. I feel like a small cog in between several large machines, spinning with all that the past has done for us.

PICTURE CREDITS

BBC Worldwide would like to thank the following for providing photographs for the plate sections and for permission to reproduce copyright material. While every effort has been made to trace and acknowledge copyright holders, we would like to apologize should there have been any errors or omissions.